Marshall Walker

The Nature of
Scientific Thought

Prentice-Hall, Inc. A SPECTRUM BOOK *Englewood Cliffs, N.J.*

Marshall Walker, a native of upstate New York, took his B.Chem. and A.M. at Cornell University. He has worked as physicist and chemist in industry and for the armed services. After the war he was a Teaching Fellow at M.I.T. and a Research Assistant at the Pennsylvania State University, from which he received his Ph.D. Since 1950 he has been on the staff of the Physics Department of the University of Connecticut, where he is currently Associate Professor and Acting Head of Department. In 1957, on the retirement of Professor G. S. Torrey, he was invited to teach a course entitled "The Nature of Scientific Thought" which provided a testing ground for this book.

© 1963 by Prentice-Hall, Inc.
Englewood Cliffs, N.J.

*Library of Congress Catalog
Card No.:* 63-9519

PRINTED IN THE UNITED STATES OF AMERICA
61066-C

Preface

This book is addressed to those who wish to learn the basic purpose and procedure common to all the sciences. The purpose is *prediction*, and the procedure consists in the construction and use of *conceptual models*. For the moment the reader may regard the word *model* as an approximate synonym for the word *theory*. The first six chapters introduce the concept of *model*, and discuss its relationship to science, mathematics, and philosophy. The next three chapters provide examples of the influence of physical, biological, and social factors upon models. Chapter X provides the mathematical vocabulary used in subsequent sections. Chapters XI through XIV illustrate how the concept of model may be used in four different fields. Finally, Chapter XV uses the vocabulary and point of view developed in this book to discuss the current and future problems of science. Following each chapter (except the last) is a brief *argument*, which is partly summary and partly justification for the contents of the chapter. The reader who already has an adequate technical vocabulary can get a bird's-eye view of the book by reading only the preface and the arguments. The general reader can use the arguments for review.

This book is written for the general, educated reader, and no previous knowledge of science or mathematics is assumed. In recent years there has been much discussion of the "two cultures"—scientific and literary—and the lack of communication between them. This book is a calculated attempt to bridge that gap, to explain science to those who read and write literature. Of course this is only half the bridge, a one-way lane. The other half, which explains literature to the scientist, must be provided by someone from the literary side. The reader of literary works does not expect his reading to be effortless; he expects to exert himself to understand what the author is saying. Those reading about science must make a similar effort. In writing about science one must refer to the philosophy of science, but this book is not intended to be a traditional approach to the philosophy of science; such books are available from specialists.

This book may best be regarded as a map. It will show the beginner where he can go, and it will show the specialist where he has been. Topics, like mountain ranges, are located and named. Sometimes they are described in considerable detail. The author makes no apology for his brief references to difficult matters. The reader must meet a concept for the first time somewhere, and where better than on a map of the region? Technical terms which are being defined explicitly or implicitly are italicized. Science has its own vocabulary, and it is necessary to learn new words and new meanings for old words if one wishes to understand science.

This book is not greatly concerned with allotting credit to specific individuals for their contributions. The validity of scientific thought does not rest on the authority of individuals, but on the authority of empirical observation. Names of individuals are used mostly as conventional designations for areas of thought. *Newtonian mechanics*, for example, now refers not only to the ideas enunciated by Newton on the basis of work by Galileo, Brahe, Kepler, and others, but also includes the later developments by Lagrange, Laplace, Hamilton, Jacobi, and many others. Science is a highly cooperative effort. As Newton put it, "If I seem to be able to see farther than others, it is because I stand on the shoulders of giants." It is a romantic oversimplification of the history of science to credit progress solely to the efforts of the great men of science.

This book assumes that the reader knows little mathematics. It must be understood, therefore, that only a description of science is possible, and a very clumsy description at that. As Latin was the scholarly language of the Renaissance, so mathematics is the scholarly language of sophisticated thought today. In the fifteenth century, a man ignorant of Latin and Greek was barred from the intellectual life of his time. Today a man ignorant of mathematics is barred from the most sophisticated intellectual life of this time. The writer, historian, poet, or philosopher who tries to comprehend the *Zeitgeist* of modern times without a knowledge of higher mathematics is as handicapped as a blind painter. Henry Adams knew this, and censured his university for condoning the pretense of an education which occurs when the student neglects mathematics. The humanist who knows no mathematics is as great a menace to society as the technologist who knows no humanities.

The relationship between mathematics and science can be stated very simply, but the statement will have little meaning unless the reader already has a rather sophisticated view of mathematics and science. This point of view is described in the first three chapters for science, and in the fourth chapter for mathematics. Many readers will find that these chapters do not agree at all with their previous conceptions of science and mathematics. Such readers are requested to be patient, and to suspend judgment until they have finished the entire book. This book describes a unified approach to all branches of science, and the author must be permitted considerable liberty in the generalization of some concepts and the oversimplication of others if such unity is to be achieved.

In order to orient the reader, the point of view of the first four chapters is summarized here and now. Science is concerned with prediction of events in the physical and biological universe. Mathematics is concerned with operations on abstract symbols, and has no necessary connection whatever with the universe. Scientists use mathematics to make predictions by choosing mathematical symbols and operations which correspond empirically to measurements obtained from the universe.

Thirteen of the fifteen chapters in this book are fairly easy to read. This facility is somewhat deceptive, and the reader is warned that he should not underestimate the complexity of the ideas described. Many apparently simple statements could be expanded and commented upon for several pages. The author has usually resisted the temptation to expound at length in order that the reader may not lose his view of the forest because of the fascinating individual trees.

Two of the chapters (IV and X, on mathematics) contain sections which are hard to read. This book is especially intended for those who are not versed in mathematics, and these chapters try to convey some very sophisticated ideas without attention to detail. The attempt may be compared to a sight-seeing trip through Switzerland by a person who knows none of the local languages. The general reader is advised to plow straight through these chapters the first time without stopping or concerning himself with understanding. If the reader finds the material interesting, he can then review as much as he wishes. Mathematicians, who are perfectionists by trade, will be horrified by this attempt to describe briefly concepts which require years of preparation when approached by the usual sequence of college courses. The author is here trying to appeal to the reader's curiosity and imagination, and is not greatly concerned with how much or how little technical knowledge the reader acquires.

Chapters XII and XIII show how the concept of model may be used in biology and sociology. These chapters are not concerned with describing the scientific or philosophic content of biology and sociology. The author has no competence for such a task, and it is irrelevant to the intention of this book. The author has tried merely to illustrate by a few examples how biologists and sociologists could use the concept of model if they thought it useful.

The process of introducing a new vocabulary and a new point of view into a scientist's description of his own work will certainly introduce inaccuracy as well. The reader who wants to know exactly what Sigmund Freud said about the id must read Freud's own exposition. In Chapter XII there is an interpretation of Freud's concepts. It is to be hoped that the interpretation has not seriously distorted the original concepts, but it is also possible that if Freud could read the exposition he would say, "That is not what I meant at all!"

It will be noted that illustrations are more often taken from physical science than from the other sciences. The author's background accounts only partly for this practice. The plain fact is that much more has been written about the basis of physics than about the substructure of biology, psychology, or sociology. Very little material is available on the philosophic bases of these latter areas.

The style is intentionally very concise in order that the reader will not lose sight of the large view during the discussion of details. This book is an orientation rather than a treatise. Specialists will note that arguments have sometimes been omitted. This book is trying to present a point of view, not a finished system. The reader is expected to cooperate by supplying illustrative material and necessary arguments, and, in general, to validate or invalidate the model as he finds necessary.

One purpose of this book is to show scientific thought as a single monolithic structure—a science of sciences. It is a science rather than a philosophy because it uses the low-order categories of the sciences (see Chapter III) rather than the high-order categories of philosophy. Scientific thought is far more cumulative than philosophic thought. There exists a self-consistent body of material accepted in practice by almost all scientists, which constitutes scientific thought as it is today. There exists no comparable body of philosophic material accepted by almost all contemporary philosophers. Scientists usually find a modified logical empiricism the most satisfactory philosophic viewpoint for scientific purposes.

Scientific thought as it is today may be compared to present-day chemistry. Chemistry, or any other science, is a body of facts and methods and models. The chemistry of today contains all the successful models of the past and none of the unsuccessful models. As far as is known, all its facts are verifiable—the current state of science contains no specifically known errors. A chemistry textbook seldom has any interest in history. It will list eight ways of preparing oxygen without mentioning that the first method was used by Priestley in 1775 whereas the eighth was developed by scientists of the Atomic Energy Commission in 1943. These historical facts may be interesting, but they are history, not chemistry.

The chemistry of today is like a skyscraper under construction. The first thirty stories are finished and in constant use. The thirty-first floor is under construction—this is current research. Many partitions have been changed in the lower floors since they were built, and changes will be made there in the future, also. But when chemistry is studied today, one studies the building as it is now. It is well known that the structure was different in the past and will be somewhat modified in the future, but the study of these changes is not chemistry. All chemists have worked on this same building and their labors have become part of the same structure so that it is difficult to separate their contributions.

The corresponding picture for philosophy would be a collection of disconnected mansions, each built by a specific person who apparently intended to build *the* skyscraper of philosophy all by himself. Some of these structures are impressive in their beauty of design and conception, but no one of them is recognized by all as *the* skyscraper of philosophy. Scientific thought is a skyscraper like chemistry, and not a collection of diverse structures like philosophy. Scientific thought has been developed by mathematicians such as Euclid, Gauss, Riemann, Cantor, Whitehead, and Russell; by physicists such as Newton, Einstein, Dirac, and Heisenberg; by chemists such as Mendeleyev and Pauling; by biologists such as Darwin; and by thousands of other specialists. Philosophers have contributed questions and criticisms, but have seldom aided in the construction directly.

Reichenbach has suggested reasons why the philosophers have made so little contribution to science. Many of them were rationalists; that is, they believed that extensive knowledge of the physical world could be obtained from reason alone. Scientists are empiricists; they believe that knowledge of nature is validated only by observing nature. The philosophers sought certainty, particularly regarding ethics. Scientists believe that certainty is unobtainable outside mathematics, and accept probabilities in their predictions for both science and ethics. Some philosophers were not critical of obscure language, and wrote passages which defy comprehension. Many used categories such as *being* or *essence*, which are so general and abstract that it is hard to say anything specific about them.

The early philosophers encountered difficulties when they tried to attach a property, say *red*, to an object. Such attempts oversimplified the problem. The current model regards *red* as a sensation arising when a particular set of stimuli reach the brain. These stimuli depend not only on the object itself, but on its illumination, its surroundings, the nature of the intervening medium, the state of the observer's eye and nervous system, and a host of other factors. The pioneer thinkers, of course, were handicapped by lack of facts and techniques which have since been developed. They are to be judged in the light of their own times.

The statements in this book concerning science, mathematics, and philosophy are believed to represent the consensus of scientists. It would require an extensive questionnaire to ascertain whether this belief is justified.

The statements in this book concerning ethics and religion represent the personal point of view of the author. These statements are gathered together into a single chapter. The point of view presented has been reached by trying to translate theological statements into language which students of science can understand. Those who think the translation is wrong are invited to provide a different translation. Some translation is necessary because the traditional vocabulary and categories of religion convey nothing to most young scientests. They have experienced the conviction which accompanies empirical verification, and no authority other than nature can command their respect.

Acknowledgments

I wish to thank the following for permission to use copyright material published elsewhere:

Bookman Associates for the Hebrew translation quoted in Chapter IX.
The Journal of Higher Education for Tables XV-1, 2 and the pertinent textual material.
The Scientific Monthly for Figures I-1, 2 and V-1 through 6 and the pertinent textual material.
John Wiley & Sons, Inc. for Figures VIII-7, 8 and the pertinent textual material.
Professor Henry Margenau and the McGraw-Hill Book Company, Inc. for the postulates of Quantum Mechanics paraphrased in Chapter XI.
Dr. Franklin S. Cooper, The Haskins Laboratories, and the Acoustical Society of America for Figures IX-1, 2, 3 and the pertinent textual material.
Princeton University Press for the section of Chapter XIII dealing with economic models.

M.W.

Table of Contents

Chapter I

The Scientific Method

Purpose. Understanding. Definition of science. Berkeley. Model. Scientific method. Cummulativity. Certainty. Laws of nature. Young scientists. Classification. Qualitative and quantitative prediction. Models of planetary motion. Brahe. Kepler's laws. Newton's laws. Gravitational and inertial mass.

The immediate purpose of scientific thought is to make correct predictions of events in nature. The ultimate purpose is the survival of man. Some events permit very accurate predictions; the time when an eclipse of the sun will occur can be computed to a fraction of a second. Other events can be predicted only as a probability; the weather forecaster, for example, can say only that there are three chances in ten that it will rain tomorrow.

At first glance, many scientific activities do not seem to involve prediction, but a closer consideration always reveals a predictive act somewhere. The engineer who designs a suspension bridge must be able to predict the effect of windstorms and specify the strength of the cables accordingly. The bacteriologist who develops a new vaccine must be able to predict how it will affect the persons vaccinated.

Some people feel that the purpose of scientific thought is to *understand* nature, and certainly many scientists and philosophers have been led by such a desire. But what exactly is meant by the word *understand*? The word has a technical meaning to be defined in the next paragraph, but here we are concerned with its colloquial meaning. In ordinary usage the phrase "to be understood" appears to mean no more than "to be familiar and predictable." A man says he *understands* his wife when her reactions are familiar and predictable; he says he understands why the team lost the game when his knowledge of previous events could have predicted the outcome. Of course there are degrees of understanding corresponding to degrees of predictability. A man has a certain degree of understanding of an automobile when he can drive one, a higher degree of understanding when he can repair one, and a still higher degree of understanding when he can design one.

Scientists use the word *understand* in a restricted technical sense. If a specific occurrence is predicted by a law that has predicted many such occurrences accurately, then the scientist says that he *understands* that occurrence.

The scientist says he understands the falling of an apple because the details of its fall can be predicted accurately by Newton's laws of motion. Predictability adds greatly to the degree of understanding, and scientists feel that events that are not predictable are not properly understood. This point of view has caused some scientists to be dissatisfied with their understanding of certain atomic processes where predictability is restricted.

Before proceeding further it is necessary to try to define the word *science*, a task complicated by the many usages of the word. A headline on the sports page says "Kid Fargo Uses Science to K.O. Champ." The leading paragraph tells us that Kid Fargo tricked the champ into carelessness by pretending to be nearly exhausted. A magazine article has the title "Science Seeks Cause of Elm Blight." By reading the article one discovers that the staff members of a certain laboratory are doing the seeking. Many other examples will come to mind.

Clearly the word *science* is being used as a one-word substitute for any one of a whole series of different phrases that use the adjective *scientific*. The essential notion behind the various phrases is the idea of prediction. A scientific pugilist observes his opponent's habitual behavior and then predicts how to feint in order to clear the way for an effective punch. A scientific fisherman is one who can predict successfully when and where the fish will bite. Every time the word *science* or *scientific* appears, the idea of prediction is explicitly or implicitly involved.

Men have always valued the ability to predict future events, for those who can predict events can guard against them. Until the time of the philosopher and bishop, George Berkeley (1685–1753), the process of making predictions seemed clear. One merely observed the changing events of the world, noted certain regularities, and made predictions based on a future expectation of these same regularities. A scientific observer was like a man watching a battle from a high mountain. He could see the enemy cavalry advancing across the plain and predict that the tide of battle would change in a few minutes.

Bishop Berkeley pointed out that each man experiences directly only the the signals of his own five senses; it is a natural inference that there is an external world that is the source of his sensations, but the actual structure of that world is purely inferential and can never be verified directly. If we let the battle mentioned above represent the external world, then the only possible knowledge of it comes through five "telegraph lines" from five "observers" that represent the five senses. Perhaps the "thing-out-there" is more like a tape recording than an actual battle.

In everyday life and even in scientific laboratories, we tend to forget the five telegraph lines. We assume that the mental picture of the battle constructed by the brain is an accurate picture of the battle itself. The physicists of the nineteenth century described the atom with the confidence of an eyewitness describing a battle. These descriptions of the atom changed frequently as new data arrived, and eventually physicists learned to remind themselves (and others) that the atom as described in their books was a mental picture built by themselves out of fragmentary information. This picture presumably corresponded to some extent with the source of the data, but the extent of the correspondence was not known.

In 1913 Niels Bohr used the word *model* for his published description of the hydrogen atom, an apt word because models include parts the prototype lacks and exclude other parts the prototype is known to possess. A model airplane has many features of the actual airplane, but the model has no little pilot in its seat and may have a rubber-band motor instead of an airplane engine.

Scientists now find it helpful to use the word *model* for theories developed long before Bohr emphasized the necessity for this term. To return to our analogy, a scientist no longer feels that he is describing the battle as an eyewitness. The information about the battle comes to him "by telegraph." From this fragmentary information he attempts to construct a map of the battlefield, and on it to move blocks of wood that represent men, companies, and armies. This map and its blocks of wood constitute a material realization of his conceptual model of the battle. The model changes as new information arrives. The scientist observes the changing model, and tries to work out regularities and make predictions. When the model makes many successful predictions, one intuitively expects considerable correspondence between the model and the "thing-out-there," but direct verification is impossible. Except for these correspondences the model need not look at all like the battle. This is fortunate, for models of electrons and other small particles can still be constructed even though it is intrinsically impossible to "look at" an electron as one looks at a virus under a powerful microscope.

The essential content of the concept of model is the existence of a correspondence between the model itself and the prototype, and a single correspondence is often enough to provide a very useful model. For example, eleven circles on a sheet of paper constitute a much-used geometric model of a football team. The circles on their paper share just one property with the football players on their playing field—mobility in two dimensions—yet this single correspondence allows the coach to make predictions about the coming game. "This particular pattern of movement [a play] by our players will probably produce a position pattern of the other team that will permit an end-run." The eleven circles do not look at all like the eleven players, but this fact is quite irrelevant to the purpose of the model.

The tackling dummy constitutes a material model of a football player because its inertia corresponds to the inertia of the player. The coach can use it to make predictions. "If our 140-pound center tends to bounce off the tackling dummy, he will probably bounce off an opposing player also." The dummy may look somewhat like a football player, but such a resemblance is irrelevant.

Models do not always have to be invented or constructed, but they do have to be recognized. A biologist can make useful predictions by regarding the nervous system of a simple animal as a model of the nervous system of a man. Norbert Wiener tells of a physiologist who recognized in an electronic scanning circuit a model of the fourth layer of the visual cortex of the brain. In such models the lack of correspondence is often as educational as the correspondences themselves.

The word *model* in a particular sentence may refer to one or more of many related aspects of the general notion. Thus *cortical model* refers to the model as it is recorded in the structure and arrangement of molecules in the memory banks of the brain. *Conceptual model* refers to the mental "picture" of the model that is introspectively present when one thinks about the model. This "picture" probably corresponds to some scanning process over the appropriate memory banks. The *verbal model* consists of the spoken or written description of the model. The *postulational model* is a certain type of verbal model that consists of a list of the postulates of the model. The *geometrical model* refers to the diagrams or drawings that are used to describe the model. The *mathematical model* refers to the equations or other relationships that provide the quantitative predictions of the model. The *material model* is the arrangement and interactions of fundamental particles, their fields and aggregates. When a writer refers to the "Bohr model of the hydrogen atom," he may have in mind any or all of these aspects; the reader must select the aspects appropriate to the context.

The main purpose of a model is to make predictions. If a mathematical model predicts future events accurately, there is no necessity for any interpretation or visualization of the process described by the equation. Many of the equations used in modern physics can be interpreted in several ways, yet the predictions are accurate despite the variety of interpretations (specific examples will be given later). However, the interpretations and visualization of a mathematical model may be very useful in the art of constructing new models.

How do men construct models? It is a common misconception that new models are constructed by strict logical deduction from observed facts and from previous models. However, this method is not used because nothing new can ever be obtained by deduction. The conclusion of a deductive process is merely an explicit statement of a fact already inherent in the information provided (this will be discussed in Chapter III).

New models are not deduced, they are *postulated*. That is, the statements that describe the model are assumed, and predictions are made from them. These predictions are checked against the measurements or observations of the actual events in nature. If the predictions are accurate, the model is successful and is said to be *validated*. If the predictions are not accurate, the model is replaced or adjusted until accurate predictions result. Scientists do not expect a model to be permanently successful because more extensive or more accurate experimental measurements are likely to be made. The predictions of the model then become inadequate or inaccurate, making it necessary to adjust the model or to construct a new one.

Scientific knowledge—that is, the experimental facts and conceptual models current at a given time—is constantly subject to revision. The formulation of the postulates of new models is an act of creation and is subject to no limitations of method. The scientist uses any and all means, conscious and unconscious, in the act of creation. The means may even be illogical, for the subsequent method of validation will eliminate the models that fail to meet the criterion of successful prediction.

Although the invention of new models is subject to no restriction of method, the validation of new models that is required in the continual revision of scientific knowledge follows a single, recurrent pattern, which has been abstracted from the historical records that describe the development of scientific theories in the past. This pattern is *not* a recipe for making new discoveries in science—it is a method for validating the new models *after* they have been postulated during the process of constant revision that characterizes scientific knowledge. This recurrent pattern is called the *scientific method*.

Summing up what has been said thus far: the purpose of scientific thought is to postulate a conceptual model of nature from which the observable behavior of nature may be predicted accurately. The formulation of new postulates is an act of creation and is subject to no limitations of method. The validation of the model, however, follows a regular pattern which has been called the *scientific method*.

The scientific method

(1) postulates a model based on existing experimental observations or measurements;

(2) checks the predictions of this model against further observations or measurements;

(3) adjusts or replaces the model as required by the new observations or measurements.

The third step leads back to the first step, and the process continues without end. No claim is made about the "reality" of the model; the sole criterion is successful prediction from the simplest, most convenient, or most satisfying model.

A common notion is that scientific knowledge is certain and unchanging, yet it has just been stressed that scientific models are constantly "subject to change without notice." These two ideas appear to be mutually contradictory. How are they to be reconciled? The answer lies in a closer consideration of the kind of changes that are made in the models.

Scientific thought is cumulative; that is, the current model includes all the successful parts of previous models. In mathematical models this cumulativity means that the old model is a *special case* of the new one. The new model does everything the old one did, and more too.

There is a constantly increasing core of unchanging ideas within the changing models. The situation is quite similar to the annual change of automobile styles. Next year's automobile design may be superficially quite different from the current style, yet everyone knows that next year's style will have wheels, a motor, a steering device, and all the essentials of this year's style. Perhaps a time will come when the wheels will be replaced by an air jet, but whatever does replace the wheels will still serve the same purpose. The basic design of a car is prescribed by its purpose; the methods of achieving this purpose may vary greatly, but the essential design changes hardly at all. In the same way, there are common factors within scientific models that remain essentially unchanged, and it is these factors that have given rise to the notion that scientific knowledge is fixed and permanent.

The notion that scientific knowledge is *certain* is an illusion. A scientist, explicitly or implicitly, assumes the existence of a universe external to himself that is the source of his sensations. He notices certain regularities in his sensations, and infers that there are regularities in the behavior of the universe. He calls these regularities of the external universe *laws of nature* and attempts to represent them by mathematical models, which have become progressively more successful in accurate predictions. It is tempting to infer that the model is beginning to resemble the *thing-out-there*, but such an inference can never be verified. No prediction can be known to be certain— nature may deviate from the model without prior notice, and it is in this sense that scientific knowledge is never certain.

New models are often quite radically different from their predecessors and often require the abandonment of ideas that have long been considered obvious and axiomatic. New models thus tend to sound like nonsense, even to other scientists, and almost all new models have been originated by comparatively young researchers. Seemingly, most workers beyond their thirties cannot "unlearn" their axioms convincingly enough to introduce radically new ideas. Furthermore, the older scientists seldom develop much aptitude in the use of the new models, even when they try to cooperate completely with the newer point of view. Extensive data on the productivity of young thinkers have been gathered by H. C. Lehman.[*]

Creative thinkers are born, not made, and start showing their ability when young. Although they often have a long and productive life, their most original ideas are produced when they are in or near their twenties. Galileo formulated the law of the pendulum when he was eighteen. Newton originated his idea of universal gravitation at twenty-four. Galois revolutionized mathematics by his development of the theory of groups before his death at the age of twenty-one. Einstein, Dirac, and Heisenberg all originated their greatest theories while in their twenties.

Creative thinkers are not the products of any planned educational process—they just happen. The formal educational system is not oriented toward creative thinkers and is more likely to retard than to help them; individual

[*] H. C. Lehman, *Age and Achievement* (Philadelphia: American Philosophical Society, 1953).

teachers, however, often rise to the occasion and provide the needed under-standing, encouragement, and advice. But the age limit on creativity is presumably effective also for the creative efforts of more ordinary people. Hence it is vital that the school system be capable of educating a promising student to the boundary of knowledge in his field while he is still young.

The postulation of a model presupposes a good supply of reliable experi-mental results. The gathering of such facts and the assignment of appro-priate nomenclature make up the descriptive phase of the scientific process. The facts are then classified. This classification itself constitutes the postu-lation of a model of the structure of nature. The biologist who can classify an animal as a member of the class of Reptilia from external features can then predict with some reliability the internal features of the animal al-though he has not yet seen them. Classification systems are abstract models, and actual animals may be found that are intermediate between classes; whether or not this situation requires a modification of the system is a matter to be determined by the consensus of researchers concerned.

The accuracy of measurements made in gathering the original facts limits the accuracy of predictions. Observations that do not contain numbers are called *qualitative*; from qualitative observations one can make only qualita-tive predictions—for example, "It was so cold this morning my car wouldn't start—your car probably won't start either." Observations that contain numbers are called *quantitative*; from quantitative observations one can make quantitative predictions—for example, "It was sixteen below zero on my porch this morning—it must be about ten below now." A more accurate quantitative prediction is exemplified by a statement made by Niels Bohr in 1913: "The spectrum of hydrogen will be found to contain a line of wave length 1215.7 Angstroms."

Quantitative predictions may be expressed in terms of probability—for example, "There are three chances out of ten that it will rain tomorrow." Quantitative predictions often contain an estimate of the accuracy of the prediction—for example, "The solar eclipse will reach totality at 35 ± 2 seconds past noon on January 23, 1925." The number is read "thirty-five plus or minus two seconds," and means (by convention) that the probability is seven chances out of ten that the eclipse will occur between 33 and 37 seconds past noon.

No prediction of the future behavior of nature is either perfectly accurate or perfectly certain. The predictions are for the future behavior of the model, and one must always be prepared to observe experimental results that will necessitate the adjustment or replacement of the model. Predictions of the behavior of small particles such as electrons can only be made in terms of probabilities (this will be discussed later).

The scientific method is an abstraction from recorded history. As a spe-cific example of such history, we shall consider the changing models of the starry sky, starting with the earliest recorded models. Men noticed very early that the stars occurred in fixed patterns, and these patterns moved across the sky as the night advanced. The Greeks constructed a model in which the stars were lights fastened to the inside of a big, hollow sphere—the sky—and this sphere rotated about the earth as a center. This model predicts that all the stars will remain fixed in their constellation patterns. However, a few of the brightest stars were seen to wander about among the constellations. These "wanderers" (*planets*, in Greek) were not predicted by the single sphere model, so the model had to be modified by providing one sphere for the stars and one sphere each for the planets.

When the planets were watched systematically, it was found that sometimes a planet would move backward for a time against the pattern of the fixed stars. This *retrograde motion* required a further change in the model. It would have been easy to regard the planet's sphere as rotating backward for a time, but this model was not acceptable to the Greeks. This rejection of the most obvious model illustrates the subjective element present in the choice of models. Models must not only predict accurately, they must also be acceptable to the prevailing taste of the times. The Greeks, of course, did not feel that they were making models. They regarded their statements as actual descriptions of reality. To them, the circle was a perfect figure and it was unthinkable that the universe should include imperfect motions. In order to explain (that is, predict) retrograde motion, they invented the ingenious model of *epicycles*, which preserved the idea that basic motions in nature must be made up of circular motions. In this model the planet itself did not move in a large circular orbit around the earth, but actually moved in a small circular orbit (an epicycle), and the center of this epicycle moved around the earth in a large circular orbit called the *deferent*. By adjusting the radii of the epicycle and the deferent, one could account for the retrograde motion, but at the expense of a rather complicated model. In Figure I-1, if you imagine yourself on the earth, it is easy to see that the planet, which usually moves from left to right against the pattern of fixed stars, moves briefly from right to left while traveling through the looped part of its orbit.

An alternative explanation of retrograde motion was included in a model constructed by Copernicus (1473–1543). He assumed that the sun was near the center of a system of circular orbits in which the earth and planets moved with fair regularity. Since anyone could see that the planets moved around the earth, this model was clearly nonsense. In time, people got used to this nonsense, and it became sensible. The retrograde motion occurs when the fast-moving earth overtakes and passes a slower-moving planet. The planet then appears to move backward as seen from the earth. The same effect is seen when a fast train overtakes a slower one.

There were still many small discrepancies between observations and the predictions of the model, but more accurate measurements were needed to convince people that the Copernican model could not be patched up to fit the observations. These accurate measurements were provided by Tycho

Brahe (1546–1601), the Danish astronomer, who made a lifelong study of the planets and gathered great quantities of measurements.

Tycho Brahe was royal mathematician to Frederick II, King of Denmark. Frederick's successor, Christian IV, withdrew this support and Brahe sought a patron outside of Denmark. The German emperor Rudolph II granted Brahe a yearly pension, and the observatory equipment was moved from

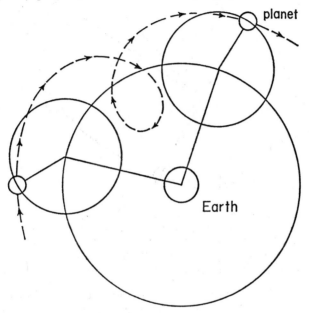

Figure I-1. In the Ptolemaic model of the solar system, each planet moves in a small circular orbit, and the center of the small circle moves in a larger circle around the earth as center.

Denmark to Prague. At Prague Johann Kepler joined his staff. Thus fate used two royal nonentities to bring together into productive symbiosis Brahe, the observer, and Kepler, the theorist. Upon Brahe's death a year later, Johann Kepler succeeded to Brahe's office as imperial mathematician. Kepler thus had available the records of Brahe's twenty years of observations of the planets and used them to formulate and check the model embodied in "Kepler's laws."

The three laws postulated by Kepler are:

(1) Each planet moves in an elliptical orbit around the sun, and one focus of the ellipse is located at the sun.

(2) The line from the planet to the sun sweeps out equal areas in equal times.

(3) The length of time needed for a planet to revolve once around the sun is called its *period*. The square of the period is proportional to the cube of the planet's greatest distance from the sun.

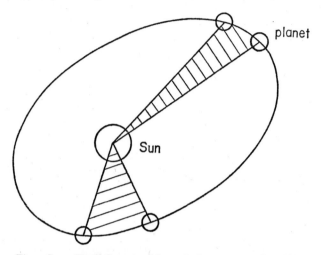

Figure I-2. Kepler's second law of planetary motion. The area (crosshatched) swept out by the radial line from sun to planet during a specified time of orbital motion (say an hour) is the same for all parts of the orbit. The ellipticity of the orbit is exaggerated: planetary orbits are nearly circular.

If these laws are assumed, then the positions of the planets can be calculated for any time, past or future. Kepler checked his predictions chiefly against observations of the planet Mars, but it was assumed that the model would be valid for the other planets as well. The predictions of this Keplerian model were so accurately validated that there was little incentive for further change in the model. The next change in model was made by Isaac Newton (1642–1727) and constituted a generalization. Kepler's laws deal only with the motion of planets in elliptical orbits. Newton's laws deal with any object moving in any sort of path. Nowadays it is known that objects moving almost as fast as light require a modification of Newton's laws, but no such objects were observable in Newton's day.

Isaac Newton believed that the motion of a falling apple and the motion of a satellite like the moon could be predicted by the same model. This statement, of course, is in modern language. Newton would say that he believed that the falling apple and the moving moon were subject to the same law of nature. Newton was twenty-four when he first started work on the problem; he was forty-four when his model became public in his famous work *Philosophiae Naturalis Principia Mathematica*, published in 1686.

The four postulates of Newton's model are given below. The first three have become known as Newton's laws of motion, and the fourth is known as Newton's law of gravitation. The laws are stated accurately, which means that several of the words used have sophisticated technical meanings. To grasp the implications of these laws one must study physics for years. The laws are presented here only to illustrate a phase in the development of models of planetary motion. Each law is discussed briefly, but the discussion is intended only to help the general reader understand what the law is trying to say.

(1) A body if at rest remains at rest, or if in motion remains in motion in a straight line at constant velocity unless acted upon by an external net force.

(2) The acceleration of a body is directly proportional to the applied force and inversely proportional to its inertial mass.

(3) If a body A exerts a force F on body B, then body B exerts on body A a force that is equal in magnitude but opposite in direction to force F.

(4) Any two objects in the universe are attracted toward each other by a force directly proportional to the product of their gravitational masses and inversely proportional to the square of the distance between their centers.

At first glance Newton's first law seems to contradict common sense. In everyday life things move only when pushed and stop moving soon after the push ceases. A croquet ball lies motionless on the grass until one strikes it; then it rolls for a distance and again comes to rest. Newton's first law seems to be saying that the ball, after being struck, should continue to move in a straight line at constant speed until some other force acts upon it. A moment's thought reminds us that the moving ball *is* being acted upon by a force—the frictional force of the surface it rolls upon. This frictional force slows it up until it comes to rest. A body such as the moon encounters almost no friction, and therefore continues to move at nearly constant speed for millions of years. The moon does not move in a straight line because of the sidewise force described in Newton's fourth law—the gravitational attraction of the earth.

Newton's second law tells quantitatively what happens when a force is applied. A force is a push or pull and can be measured by a spring scale in pounds. Imagine a body, say a large boulder, in interstellar space. It is so far away from any other object that the gravitational pull of even the earth, sun, and stars is too small to be measurable. Suppose the boulder is observed telescopically from the earth, and is measured to be moving at 2 miles per hour away from the earth. It will continue to move at 2 miles per hour in a straight line until disturbed. A force could be applied to the boulder by attaching a towline to a rocket space ship. If the ship pulls it in a direction away from the earth, then its speed will increase from 2 miles per hour to, say, 20 miles per hour; the boulder has been accelerated. Newton's second law says that a small force produces a small acceleration and a large force produces a large acceleration.

Newton's second law also refers to the *mass* of an object. Unfortunately, the same word *mass* is used to refer to two different properties of an object. Here we are interested in the *inertial* property of an object, and are concerned therefore with *inertial mass. Inertia*, of course, is that property of an object that measures its ability to resist changes in motion. In our example, a solid gold boulder (we spare no expense for illustrations) requires a much larger force to accelerate it than, say, a chunk of cork of the same size. The gold boulder has more *inertial mass* than the chunk of cork. The *inertial mass* of an object is a number, and this number can be measured on an *inertia balance* for small objects and computed from the ratio of force to acceleration for large objects. Newton's second law tells us that the acceleration of an object when subjected to a specific force is *inversely proportional* to its inertial mass; that is, a large acceleration occurs for a small mass, but a small acceleration occurs for a large mass.

Newton's third law is clear as it stands. If a book lies on the table, the earth attracts the book downward with a force called the *weight* of the book. Let us assume that the book weighs 2 pounds. At the same time the book attracts the earth upward with a force of 2 pounds. These two forces constitute an example of Newton's third law. Note that the two forces act on different objects and do not cancel each other as they would if they acted on the same object. Owing to its weight, the book exerts a downward force of 2 pounds on the table, and from Newton's third law the table exerts an upward force of 2 pounds on the book. This is a second example of Newton's third law, and these forces do not cancel.

Although there is a downward force on the book, it does not accelerate because the downward pull of the earth *on the book* is canceled by the upward push of the table *on the book* since these two forces do act on the same object. The table does not accelerate either because the downward force exerted by the book and the downward force exerted by the earth on the table are canceled by an upward force exerted by the floor on the table. If the floor cannot exert this force—say the concrete is not yet hard—then the table *will* accelerate, and sink into the soft concrete.

Newton's fourth law, the law of gravitation, involves the other use of the word *mass*. This *gravitational mass* measures quite a different property from inertia. It measures the property that objects possess of attracting each other. Strangely and unexpectedly, the numerical measures of these two properties of the same object turn out to be identical. This equality of the inertial mass and gravitational mass was checked by very accurate measurements by Roland von Eötvös in 1909. Albert Einstein (1876–1955) tells us that this equivalence suggested to him a basic feature of his theory of relativity.

These four postulates permit very accurate predictions of the motion of all sorts of objects, from the path of a falling apple to the orbit of a satellite. Newton checked the predictions of his model against observations of the motion of our great natural satellite, the moon. He also validated his model by deriving from his postulates the laws originally formulated by Kepler. This means that Newton's model includes the Keplerian model as a special case. All the successful predictions of Kepler's laws are thus automatically included in Newton's laws. This inclusion of the successful parts of old models into the new, more general, model is typical of the history of science. Kepler's model applied only to elliptical planetary orbits. Newton's model applies to all forms of orbits. The orbits of some comets, for example, are not elliptical, but the Newtonian model predicts them accurately.

It is now possible to illustrate the technical meaning of the word *understand* as used by scientists. Newton's model permits scientists to say that they *understand* Kepler's model, for scientists say they *understand* a model when they regard it as a special case of a more general model. Clearly, the most general model at a given time in history cannot be understood in this sense.

We have now traced the changing models of planetary motion to a vantage point where planetary motion is seen as a special case of all motion. Is this the end? Of course not, for no model is likely ever to be permanent. Newtonian mechanics remained essentially unchanged for over two hundred years and is still used for all predictions made on bodies that are not too small and not too fast. For particles of subatomic size—electrons, for example—Newtonian mechanics has been modified to a form termed *quantum mechanics*. For objects that move nearly as fast as the velocity of light, Newtonian mechanics has been modified by Einstein to a form termed *relativistic mechanics*. These more general models will be discussed in a later chapter.

Argument

The purpose of scientific thought is successful prediction, which is a prerequisite of understanding. Predictions are made by constructing and extrapolating conceptual models. The construction of a model is a creative act that admits no standard procedure, but the validation of the model follows a regular process called the *scientific method*. Models are never certain and are always subject to revision, but each new model includes the successful parts of older models. Thus scientific knowledge is cumulative. The increasing generality of successive models is illustrated by the sequence of models constructed to predict the motion of planets against the background of fixed stars.

A Survival Technique

The scientific method is merely a formalization of *learning by experience*. Anything that learns by experience is using the scientific method in a primitive form. Learning by experience is not limited to humans, animals, or even living things; certain devices can learn by experience. The essential steps in the process are these:

(1) A first stimulus causes an animal (or device) to act in a specific pattern.
(2) While following this pattern, the animal or device encounters a second stimulus.
(3) This second stimulus is recorded as a *memory*.
(4) When the first stimulus is applied again, the animal or device follows a different pattern of action because of the *memory*.

As an example, consider a child who reacts to a first stimulus of thirst by drinking from his glass of milk. One day the glass is filled with buttermilk, and the child receives an unexpected second stimulus. The next time he is thirsty he may refuse his milk until convinced that it is not buttermilk.

As an example of a nonliving device that learns by experience, consider an ordinary household electric outlet and its fuse. When a household appliance is plugged in, the outlet provides the necessary electric current. This is normal behavior; it corresponds to the child habitually drinking his milk. Then one day a defective lamp is plugged in and the fuse burns out. The burnt fuse corresponds to the child's memory of the buttermilk. The outlet will no longer provide current to appliances until the memory has been removed by inserting a new fuse. Both the child and the electric circuit have "learned by experience." The brain and nerve circuits of the child are much more complicated than the electrical circuits of the electric outlet and fuse, but the same sort of process has occurred in each. In a primitive way, both the child and the electric circuit have used the scientific method and for the same purpose—self-preservation. The child's response to strange-tasting milk is part of the organism's defense mechanism against being destroyed by spoiled food. This mechanism was developed during the evolution of the human body by natural selection. The response of the fused circuit to an overload current is the circuit's defense mechanism against being destroyed by the overload. It also arose by a sort of natural selection because designers found that unfused circuits did not survive.

The phrase *scientific method* has usually been applied only to cases where it was used consciously. One tends to think of a professional scientist testing model after model until he finds a successful one. But the child with the milk is obviously using the scientific method even though he can hardly talk. He has a model based on experience and predicts from his model that the glass of white stuff will taste good. For a large number of instances his predictions are correct. Then he encounters a glass of white stuff that does *not* taste good, alters his model accordingly, and predicts that the next glass of white stuff will taste bad. And he will retain this second model until further experience leads him to modify it. It is very unlikely that he has been consciously following the steps of the scientific method. Nevertheless, it seems a reasonable inference that the steps of the scientific method have been followed automatically.

We now have three instances of the scientific method in action. The scientist is conscious himself and uses the method consciously. The child is conscious himself and uses the method automatically. The electric circuit is not conscious and uses the method automatically. The scientist and the electric circuit represent two extreme examples of the same process; between them lie a whole series of instances differing in degrees of consciousness.

It is the point of view of this chapter that the scientific method is a survival technique that developed during the biological evolution of living things. Any organism or device that includes a suitably connected memory unit can "learn by experience," and this learning by experience contains the basic elements of the scientific method. In order that the origin of the scientific method can be seen in its historical setting, we will consider briefly the current models of physical and biological evolution.

Measurements made in recent years have been extrapolated into the past to yield models of the early development of the universe. The interpretation of our astronomical measurements as numbers that describe stars and planets existing in space and time is, of course, itself a model. However, it is a model of such long standing that one tends to ascribe reality to it. In writing about such long-established models as space and time, we shall use ordinary language which regards space and time as aspects of reality, and remind the reader only occasionally that even these basic concepts are conceptual models used to correlate stimuli.

Careful measurements of the position and motion of the nearby stars show that our sun and its planets are located in one of the spiral arms of a great pinwheel of stars called the *local galaxy*. The Milky Way is our view of the stars in the arms of this galaxy. Millions of other such galaxies scattered through space can be seen on the photographs taken with the great telescopic cameras of the astronomical observatories. The nearest of these other spiral nebulas can be seen with the naked eye in the constellation Andromeda.

The common unit of distance, the mile, is much too small for use in expressing astronomical distances. A more convenient unit is the *light-year*, the distance light travels in a year. Since light has a speed of 186,000 miles per second, the *light-year* is a distance of about six million million miles. Expressed in this unit, the distance from the earth to the sun is about one sixty-thousandth of a light-year, the distance to the center of our local galaxy is about 30,000 light-years, and the distance to the next nearest spiral galaxy is about two million light-years.

During the last forty years careful measurements have been made on the light coming to us from many of these distant spiral galaxies. From such measurements one can infer the distances of these galaxies. The color of light emitted by hydrogen gas in a distant galaxy is more reddish than the light emitted by hydrogen gas in a laboratory on earth. This red-shift can be interpreted in three ways: (1) the hydrogen gas observed in the distant galaxy is different from hydrogen gas on earth; (2) the light from the distant galaxy changed color during the millions of years of travel since it left the galaxy; (3) the distant galaxy is moving away from the earth at a speed of thousands of miles per second. The consensus of astronomers favors the third interpretation, presumably because such an expansion of galactic space is consistent with one of the solutions of the equations of general relativity. No direct experimental observation has yet been devised which can differentiate among the three interpretations.

According to the third interpretation, the current model of the universe pictures the galaxies as flying apart from each other. The galaxies nearest to the earth are receding at a rate of about a thousand miles per second. The more distant galaxies recede progressively faster as the distance increases. This description sounds as though all the galaxies were running away from the observer on the earth, but an observer in any other galaxy would get the same impression. Imagine a race in which all the runners start together, but run at different (but constant) speeds. From the view point of any one runner, all the other runners seem to be moving away from him—those in front seem to move forward and those behind get further behind.

It is natural to extrapolate this model backward and try to infer what the universe was like billions of years ago. This backward extrapolation can be done in two ways. If one assumes that the total amount of matter in the universe remained constant during the expansion, the Gamow model results. If one assumes that the total amount of matter in the universe increased during expansion, then the Hoyle model results. *

* See George Gamow, *The Creation of the Universe* (New York: The Viking Press, 1952), and Fred Hoyle, *Frontiers of Astronomy* (New York: Harper & Row, Publishers, 1955); both available in paperback form.

The Gamow model pictures the universe as originating in a giant explosion several thousand million years ago. At that time all the matter in the universe was packed into a small space, and the temperature was very high. The spiral galaxies as we see them today are regarded as fragments from the original explosion. The fastest galaxies are most distant because it is their great speed that took them out to such great distances in the time that has elapsed since the explosion. The slower galaxies, correspondingly, are not so far away.

The Hoyle model pictures the universe of the remote past as looking the same as the universe looks today. Although the galaxies are pictured as moving away from each other continually, matter appears in the universe and eventually forms new galaxies so that the average separation of the galaxies remains about the same. No one has yet devised a measurable experiment that can distinguish between the Hoyle and Gamow models. We will therefore leave this phase of evolution of the universe and proceed to the phase of biological evolution on the earth.

Suppose a scientist wishes to experiment with a simple form of living thing such as bacteria. First, he must arrange a place that has the right temperature for them. He usually constructs a water bath for them to grow in because it is hard to change the temperature of water, and once the temperature is set at the right value it is fairly easy to keep the temperature constant. To help keep the temperature constant he surrounds the water bath with a layer of insulating material—perhaps a wall of cork. He then provides a source of heat to keep the bath warm. He usually puts an electric immersion heater in the bath, and provides a thermostat to turn it on and off as needed. However, he could provide a heat lamp and adjust its distance from the water until the heat arriving from the lamp just balanced the heat lost by the water to the room. The water would then stay at a constant temperature until the lamp burned out or the water evaporated. He could prevent the evaporation of water by covering the tank so the evaporating water would condense and flow back into the bath.

A few hundred million years ago conditions on earth resembled such a constant temperature bath. The ocean was the water bath, the vacuum of space provided a good insulator, the sun acted as a heat lamp, and the force of gravitation returned the evaporated water to the ocean through rainfall and rivers. One should not thereby assume that our planet was designed for the support of living things. If a particular sun has a series of planets at different distances, one or more of them may be located so that the proper conditions for living things exist there. We observe that life does exist on our planet, and can only infer thereby that conditions favorable to life have existed here for some time.

The early ocean was warm, about 70° Fahrenheit. Over the ocean there was an atmosphere, which probably contained (among other gases) water vapor, methane, ammonia, and hydrogen. Lightning storms doubtless occurred then as they do now. Harold Urey and S. L. Miller have shown that electrical discharges in such a mixture of gases cause amino acids to be formed. These amino acids are the building blocks of proteins, the stuff from which all living things are constructed. Once these amino acids were present in the ocean, it was only a matter of time for chance collisions between them to build up the giant protein molecules that make up viruses and other more complicated living things.

This model has been criticized by du Noüy, who computed that the probability of a protein molecule's being formed by chance encounters is very small. The details of his calculation are not given, but it appears that the computation is for the case of building a protein molecule *in one step* by accidental placement of its constituent atoms. The resulting probability is, of course, very small. Scientists have never suggested that proteins were formed in this way. The actual process is pictured as occurring in steps, two single particles joining to become a double particle, two double particles to become a quadruple particle, and so on. The colliding particles do not even need any particular orientation in most cases since the attractive forces will pull them into the proper position. The probabilities involved are nearly certainties rather than otherwise, and an essentially similar process would occur in any organic chemistry laboratory if a complicated compound were synthesized from its elements. The chemist is useful only in producing an economic yield of a pure product. Nature dispenses with the chemist and uses low yields of impure products.

The essence of this increase in complexity is that it is a *one-way* process. Owing to the prevailing ambient temperature, components that join together *stay* together. They can easily become more complex by collision, but special conditions are needed to break them apart again. The reactions themselves are reversible, but the surrounding conditions favor the survival of the complex molecule. Some doors are built to swing either way, and people can pass through one way as easily as the other, but other conditions—say an open elevator shaft behind the door—can easily convert the two-way door into a one-way trap.

The transition from complex inert molecular aggregates to even more complex living molecular aggregates is a series of almost imperceptible steps. The self-repair, reproduction, and response to stimuli characteristic of living aggregates have been found over a considerable range of colloid and virus structures in such various degrees that the distinction between living and nonliving matter is no longer a sharp line but a diffuse region.

As time went on, these aggregates, in activity described by biological laws yet unformulated, increased in complexity and size and became adapted to wider ranges of living conditions. Some crawled out of the ocean onto the shore, and, as time went on developed into amphibians, reptiles, and mammals; some took to the air and developed eventually into birds. Despite the controversies over the details of natural selection, the basic idea is unquestioned: those structure changes that favored survival persisted. One such structure that favored survival was a device to store records of the surrounding environment. Then, when the current environment resembled a previous threat, the organism could attempt to change it by flight or attack.

This device eventually developed into the brain. The ability to predict future events obviously increases the probability of survival, and thus natural selection tends to favor the development of the brain. One can imagine a small animal running desperately from a large carnivore. By chance the little animal dashes across some swampy ground, and the large animal bogs down in the mud. The next time the small animal seeks to evade such a luncheon engagement he may streak for the nearest swamp. Competence in such elementary mental activity is well rewarded—by survival. Incompetence is also rewarded—by death. Presumably, this small ancestor of ours did not outline the steps of the scientific method as he ran, but the essential steps were there whether he was conscious of them or not.

As time went on, various living things evolved specializations that increased their probability of survival. Antelopes specialized in escape by running, cats specialized in skillful stalking, turtles specialized in armament, skunks specialized in defensive gas warfare. Man specialized in predicting the future, and the systemization of this process is called *science*. An explorer in a strange land would infer the presence of skunk from an odor in the air; he would infer the presence of man from the discovery of a scientifically designed trap: science is the stink of man.

Attributes or techniques favor survival with respect to a certain environment. If the environment changes fairly suddenly, the attributes evolved to favor survival under the old conditions may actually oppose survival under the new conditions. An animal that has adapted to desert conditions may die if the desert, through some geologic cataclysm, becomes a swamp. An elderly immigrant may bury his money in the traditional way to keep it safe. In his new country it would probably be safer to keep it in a bank. He intends to keep his money safe, but it is his behavior, not his intention, that influences the probability of safety. Although all normal behavior is intended to favor survival, an act may actually oppose survival if the actor is unaware of new factors in the situation.

Science, like all other weapons of survival, is a double-edged tool. The same knowledge that can be used to help society survive can be used to destroy it. A small dose of radiation can sometimes retard cancer; a large dose of radiation can kill the patient. Any survival technique can be misused and become a technique of destruction.

The human organism has drawn far enough ahead in its race for survival so that the luxury of *comfort* is possible. Comfort is the state of an organism when there appears to be no immediate threat to its survival. A man is said to be in "comfortable circumstances" when his physiological and psychological needs of the moment and forseeable future seem assured. Clearly, the man must have well-validated knowledge of his immediate and future needs or his "comfort" will be an illusion. The unprotected happy moron does not live long.

In the everyday life of man today, the desire for survival takes on the more sophisticated form of the desire for comfort. The natural selection that favored the development of the brain in the struggle for bare survival still favors the development of the brain today when man is engaged in the competition of economic and social survival. The degree of comfort, provided it is not an illusion, is a measure of successful competition because the degree of comfort measures the probability of future survival.

The scientific method is valued by man because it contributes to man's struggle for survival as an individual and as a species, and beyond survival to man's desire for comfort. Clearly the society that can predict what vaccine will kill poliomyelitis virus is more likely to survive (other things being equal) than the society that cannot make such predictions.

The operation of the brain is a rapid repetition of the cycle of the scientific method applied to successive instantaneous situations. A child who wants to cross the street predicts that he can do so before the approaching truck arrives and then submits his prediction to experimental validation. The brain processes of an Einstein as he works on the unified field theory differ only in degree from the brain processes of the child crossing the street. The method is essentially the same in both instances, and both processes persist because they increase the probability of survival of the individual and the species.

Argument

The scientific method is a formalization of the process of learning by experience. Any organism or device with a memory can learn by experience. The operation of the brain of any living thing is a rapid, automatic repetition of the basic steps of the scientific method applied to successive instantaneous situations. Some men use the scientific method consciously, but the same basic process goes on in men and animals automatically in everyday life. The scientific method is a survival technique that first appeared in primitive form in the first organism that included a memory. As the brain and nervous system increased in complexity through evolutionary processes, the sophistication of the scientific method increased. Man has the most complex brain and nervous system known, and the scientific method in its most sophisticated form is used by man as he strives for survival and comfort.

Science and Philosophy

*Categories. Reduction of categories. Order and interaction. **Deduction**. Induction. Hypothetico-deductive method. Operational definition. Absolute time. Metaphysical presuppositions.*

The single word *philosophy* originally referred to all serious and formal study carried on by the human brain. As knowledge increased, men began to specialize in certain areas of endeavor, and such areas received their own names: *mathematics, theology, physics,* and a score of others. Thinking men raised questions, and these questioners were called *philosophers.* Other men developed techniques to answer these questions, but these answerers were no longer called philosophers; they were called *mathematicians, chemists,* or *physicists.* Thus, unjustly, philosophy now seems to be the region of unanswered questions and science the region of answers. The reader who tends to regard such a statement as an implicit definition must be reminded of a similar statement made about a famous Master of Balliol: "What he didn't know wasn't knowledge."

It is the point of view of this essay that one can classify a man as philosopher or scientist by examining the *categories* he uses for his models. A *category* is defined as a basic concept or its physical referent used for the construction of models. The word as defined here does *not* have its common meaning of group or class, and it does *not* refer to certain concepts used by Kant. The word is defined here in accordance with its contemporary technical usage. This modern usage is illustrated in Table III-1, which lists a few representative categories for different fields of endeavor. The categories are listed in order of complexity: nuclei are aggregates of protons and neutrons, atoms are aggregates of nuclei and electrons, molecules are aggregates of atoms, and so on. Note that the word *molecule* may refer to the mental concept (an elementary conceptual model) and thus have mental existence, or it may refer to the "thing-out-there" which is postulated as the source of our measurements and thus has physical existence. The words *point, justice,* etc., are pure abstractions; they have mental existence but not physical existence. Of course, all concepts (which have mental existence) can exist only if there is some corresponding physical structure (an arrangement of molecules) in the cortex of the brain. In this sense all categories that have mental existence also have cortical existence, a particular kind of physical existence. Several such categories, often of different levels, are used to construct predictive models. Thus a physiologist building a model of the brain might find it convenient to use categories from biology, chemistry, and physics.

Table III-1

Order of Categories

Mental existence and cortical existence	*Field*
3. Extrapolations: perfect justice, divinity, etc.	Theology
2. Universals: justice, beauty, holiness, etc.	Philosophy
1. Mathematical concepts: points, lines, etc.	Mathematics

Physical and mental existence	
10. Groups of animals	Sociology
9. Animals with highly developed communication	Anthropology
8. Animals with little communication	Zoology
7. Ego, id, subconscious, etc.	Psychology
6. Organs: heart, liver, brain, etc.	Physiology
5. Simple organisms: cells, protozoa, etc.	Biology
4. Giant molecules; viruses	Biochemistry
3. Molecules	Chemistry
2. Atoms	Physics
1. Nuclei	Physics
0. Fundamental particles: electron, proton, etc.	Physics

The categories that give a man satisfaction are basic to his thinking and determine whether he becomes, say, a chemist or a philosopher. It is doubtful if a man has any conscious choice regarding these categories. The choice is made for him automatically by his genetic inheritance, the intellectual atmosphere surrounding his youth, his early reading, and other personal experiences. Formal education as a whole is fairly neutral and does not try to recommend any particular set of categories. On the other hand, an individual teacher often exerts great influence through his enthusiasm for his field. The levels of categories that give a man satisfaction are usually determined before he is twenty and seldom change thereafter.

A man becomes a philosopher because he finds pleasure in building conceptual models using abstract general categories such as justice, being, essence, and the like. A man becomes a chemist because explanations in terms of molecular structure convey conviction and satisfaction to him. The chemist seldom derives any satisfaction from the philosophical categories. The explanations philosophers advance in their fields do not seem to the chemist to be explanations at all. To the chemist, the philosopher seems like an incompetent dreamer who does not even realize that his categories are so vague and general that they are useless for precise thinking. To the philosopher, the chemist seems like a boy building models with an Erector set: the models work, but they do not directly answer the questions that concern the philosopher.

In a general way a scientist tolerates those who use categories lower (less complex) than his own, and questions the intellectual competence of those who use categories of higher order. It is probably impossible for a man to change his level of categories upward. The physicist who works as a chemist thinks best in terms of his own physical categories. If the problem is too complicated for such categories, he becomes restless and abandons the problem. Physicists who blunder into philosophy bring their categories with them and ignore the categories of the natives. Communication between them is almost impossible and the social amenities suffer.

Models of nature are built starting at any level of categories, but these models are unconvincing to people who use lower-order categories. Biochemists are not satisfied with explanations that use the categories of psychology, and both biochemists and psychologists criticize the models of the sociologists.

Occasionally, as science advances, it is found that a category of one level is a composite of categories of a lower level. For example, the purpose of the early chemists was to analyze substances into their basic constituents. Thus, water was shown to be separable into hydrogen and oxygen, salt was separated into sodium and chlorine, and so on for thousands of substances. Eventually the early chemists made up a growing list of substances—hydrogen, oxygen, chlorine, and so forth—that they could not separate into simpler parts. They called these substances *chemical elements* and concluded that all other substances were made of combinations of the eighty or so *elements* on their list. Thus the *element* was a basic category of chemistry. When the physicists of the early twentieth century developed a successful model of the atom of each element, it became possible for the chemist to regard his basic category, the element, as a composite structure of categories of a lower order—protons, neutrons, and electrons. This occurrence is called a *reduction of categories*. Table III-1 implies that the categories of a particular level are simply composites of the categories of the next lower level. Thus molecules are simply combinations of atoms, cells are combinations of molecules, and so on.

The implication that a living cell is simply an ordered combination of molecules raises a question that has been argued for generations. If one duplicates exactly the structure of a living cell, will the resulting construction also be alive? Some biologists have said *yes*; others, *no*. The biologists who say *no* are called *vitalists* because their model of the cell requires a mysterious *vital principle* or *vital force* to be present if the cell is to be "alive." We can now reword the "vitalist controversy" into a new form. The vitalists say that the categories of biology *cannot* be reduced to the categories of chemistry. For a definite answer one must wait and see. If the vitalist means that biology cannot be expressed in terms of the categories known to chemistry today, he may well be right. If the vitalist means that biology can never be expressed in terms of the categories of chemistry, he is making more of a prediction than most scientists consider advisable. Limiting the possibilities of the future has never been a safe procedure. Most scientists will continue to expect the possible reduction of all categories until confronted with well-authenticated cases of its impossibility.

The vitalist controversy has included much discussion of a related question: "Is the whole equal to the sum of its parts?" The whole certainly may have aspects that the individual parts cannot have. *Order* is the commonest example. A single marble has no such property as order if we disregard its internal structure, but three marbles do have order. They can be arranged in a straight line, an equilateral triangle, or many other ways. Order is a property of an aggregate but not of a single structureless element of the aggregate. A second property of an aggregate that has no meaning for a single structureless element is *force of interaction,* or loosely, *interaction.* The gravitational force of attraction between two or more material objects is an example of such interaction. When a scientist builds a model using several objects (the sun and planets, for example), the possibility of order and interaction occurs automatically. The aggregate may then have properties that are quite unexpected from a naïve consideration of the properties of the isolated constituent parts. These properties of the aggregate, however, are considered as latently present in each of the isolated constituents even though such properties are unobservable while the constituent is isolated. The force of gravitation of the earth is considered a property of the earth even though it could not be observed unless a second object (say an apple or a satellite) were present to indicate the attraction.

The various phenomena of living organisms are regarded as properties of the order and interactions of the atoms that make up the proteins and other constituents of protoplasm. It is possible that properties of aggregates other than those mentioned will be needed for a successful model of a living cell. When a well-established need for such a property is encountered, the property will be postulated.

Early attempts were made to explain scientific thought by means of the process of *deduction*. In this essay *deduction* is defined to refer only to reasoning from the general to the particular, from the class to the member of the class. "Each member of the class of all men is mortal; Socrates is a member of the class of all men, therefore Socrates is mortal." This syllogism is a familiar example of the deductive process. The procedure is sound intuitively; it is impossible to imagine true premises followed by a false conclusion. The process, however, has two difficulties in practice: (1) the truth or acceptibility of the premises must be established separately; (2) the process provides no new knowledge. The conclusive statement that Socrates is mortal is just a shortened version of the stated premise that Socrates is a member of the class of mortal men. Science is trying to validate new knowledge. The process of deduction is not enough by itself to account for the new knowledge accumulated by science. Deduction is chiefly useful in mathematics where premises can be accepted as true by definition.

A later attempt was made to explain scientific thought by means of the process of *induction*. By induction one reasons from particular cases to the general case. "Each of the seven coins in my pocket has a date later than 1930; therefore all coins have dates later than 1930." This procedure is not sound intuitively; it seems quite possible that all coins do not have dates later than 1930. The process gives something new, but the new statement is not necessarily true. Induction alone is not enough to account for science. Statements may be made by induction, but they can be validated only by experience.

The method actually used by science is a combination of induction, inspiration, and deduction; it is called the *hypothetico-deductive* method, and has been already discussed and illustrated. By induction and inspiration the scientist postulates a model. From this model he deduces predictions. If these predictions are verified by further observations, then the model has been *validated*. The word *proved* is reserved for mathematics; models are said to be *validated* by experience. *Validated* in this technical sense is intended to imply only that the model has previously made correct predictions. It is rather expected that the model will continue to predict as accurately as it has in the past, but there is no guarantee of such behavior. The word *proved* implies too much certainty and permanence to be used in describing models. The word *true* is used only to apply to statements where empirical verification is possible. The statement, "These roses are red," may be labeled as true (or false) by looking at the roses. A model is not said to be true or false; it is said to be validated or unvalidated. Similarly, the word *truth* is applied only to statements, not to models. All of these careful usages are intended to help the reader gain a clearer picture of the purposes and achievements of scientific thought.

The hypothetico-deductive process is familiar to many unsuspecting readers under another name. Sherlock Holmes used the hypothetico-deductive process continually, and just as continually misnamed it "deduction." A reading of any passage where Holmes is "making deductions" shows that he is using the scientific method. For example, Holmes observes that an elderly man has a commanding air, a military haircut, and an anchor tattooed on one hand. He assumes a model to correlate these data, and predicts that the man is a retired marine sergeant. Dr. Watson then validates the model by direct inquiry. Sherlock Holmes also illustrates nicely that the postulation of a model requires inspiration. Such inspiration does not come easily to everybody; Dr. Watson never became very adept at the process.

The categories, concepts, and quantities used in science are defined *operationally*. That is, a quantity such as length or mass is defined (that is, specified) by the series of operations used in measuring the quantity. The phrase "length of a desk" is defined to mean the number read from a standard scale laid alongside the edge of the desk. The phrase "mass of an object" is defined to mean the sum of the numbers on the standard masses that will exactly balance the object when placed on an analytical balance.

The name *operational definition* was given by P. W. Bridgman, who stressed the necessity for that procedure in science. Most of the quantities in science had been defined (specified) operationally from the beginning so that no extensive reformulation was necessary. The operations involved may be physical, mental, or both. Thus an operational definition of *density* requires the physical operation of determining the mass of the object, the physical determination of its dimensions, the mental computation of its volume, and the mental operation of dividing the mass by the volume.

The operational point of view does not forbid the use of hypothetical operations, but it does require that such operations be realizable. A concept defined by operations which cannot actually be performed may have some use in discourse, but that concept will not usually inspire enough confidence to be acceptable to most scientists unless it provides very reliable predictions.

As an example of the contribution of the operational point of view to physics, we shall consider the attempts to establish an *absolute simultaneity* of time at different places.

To be specific, let us try to synchronize two watches, one at Greenwich and one on Mars. Only in the last century has the difficulty of such synchronization become apparent; previously all scientists had assumed the synchronization was possible. Newton, for example, assumed an *absolute time*, that is, that watches anywhere in the universe could be synchronized with some chosen standard watch. Intuitively, it seems obvious that one ought to be able to adjust watches anywhere in the universe so they will indicate the "same" time. It is a valuable contribution of the operational point of view that the intuitively obvious, in this instance, is an illusion.

The simplest way to synchronize watches on the earth and on Mars would seem to be to synchronize two watches on the earth and then take one to Mars. In order to take one watch to Mars, it is necessary to accelerate the watch and then decelerate it upon arrival. All watches have moving parts, and it is well known that acceleration affects moving parts seriously. Furthermore, one has no confidence in being able to compute the effect of the acceleration on the watch. Even if the watch were brought back from Mars and found to check exactly with the earth watch, one could not be sure that the trip to Mars had not caused a deviation that the trip back somehow had canceled. It seems necessary to abandon this method.

The second attempt starts with one watch at Greenwich and a second watch on Mars. At exactly midnight on the Greenwich watch a powerful light is flashed. The observer on Mars watches for the flash, and starts his own watch. If the Mars observer could then subtract the time interval required for the light signal to travel from the earth to Mars, the watches could be synchronized. The computation of this time interval requires one to divide the distance of Mars from Greenwich by the velocity of light over that path.

The distance from Greenwich to Mars is known, although not very accurately. The velocity of light has been measured quite accurately; however, all the accurate measurements of the velocity of light over a distance have been measured for the "round trip" of 44 miles from Mt. Wilson to Mt. San Antonio and back to Mt. Wilson. A one-way measurement of the velocity would require two synchronized watches, one on Mt. Wilson and one on Mt. San Antonio. But the synchronization of watches at different places is our original problem. We have gone a full circle and ended where we started.

There is one possibility still open. If it is assumed that light travels at the same velocity from Mt. Wilson to Mt. San Antonio as it does on the way back, then the watches can be "synchronized." The quotation marks are used to remind us that this type of "synchronization" is not operational; it has been obtained only at the cost of using an unverifiable postulate. No one has yet been able to invent a sequence of operations that can synchronize watches at different places without using some unverified postulate. The notion of *absolute time* is not operational.

Other contributions of the operational point of view have already been illustrated in Chapter II, where it was noted on several occasions that no experimental (that is, operational) procedure could distinguish among various models or various interpretations of a single model. The operational point of view has also served science well in pointing out certain instances in which no operational *invalidation* of a proposed model appears to be possible. Such instances can occur in fields like sociology, where precise quantitative predictions are not often attainable, and the validation (or invalidation) of a model is not so definite as in the physical sciences.

Many subjects that are often found under the general heading of "philosophy of science" are not included in this chapter because the general ideas of relativity and quantum mechanics are needed to discuss them properly. Causality and determinism, for example, will be discussed later when a more adequate vocabulary has been developed. We shall conclude this chapter with a brief consideration of the word *metaphysics*.

The word *metaphysics* has fallen into disrepute among scientists. The term was coined by Andronicus of Rhodes (c. 70 B.C.) to refer to an untitled book of Aristotle. This book seemed to be sequel to Aristotle's book *Physics*, so Andronicus referred to the sequel as "next-beyond-physics" or *meta-physics*. Traditionally, *metaphysics* is defined as "the science of being as such," a phrase too general to be of much help.

In scientific writing the word *metaphysical* means "not subject to empirical validation." Scientists today are so permeated with the necessity of empirical validation that they are insulted if anyone describes their models as *metaphysical*. Of course there must be certain unproved or unvalidated assumptions at the beginning of any thought sequence. At the basis of any branch of mathematics lie certain unproved assumptions that make up the *axioms* of that branch. At the beginning of a book on elementary geometry are listed the axioms of geometry; for example, "Through any two points only one straight line can be drawn." Similarly, at the basis of science are several unvalidated presuppositions which may be called the axioms of science. These axioms (stated and unstated) are sometimes termed the metaphysical presuppositions of science. Scientists do not usually try to isolate and state these basic hypotheses. Philosophic writers try to infer them from the writings of the scientists. Extensive books have been written on the subject, and our purpose here is only to provide a few examples of such basic presuppositions:

(1) It is assumed that, beyond the sensations of normal observers, there exists a common source (the universe) of these sensations and that the behavior of this source is regular enough so that events may be predicted.

(2) It is assumed that successful prediction is to be accepted as the criterion of a valid model.

(3) It is assumed that the brain and nervous systems of normal observers interact in a fairly regular way with the universe so that there is direct correspondence between events of the universe and sensations of the brain and nervous system.

The justification for these and other assumptions lies in the utility of science in contributing to the survival and comfort of man as an individual and as a species.

Argument

A *category* is a basic unit used for the construction of a model. Each science or field of thought has a characteristic level of category. Table III-1 arranges representative examples of such categories into order according to the complexity of structure of each category. The categories that give a man satisfaction as explanations are basic to his thinking and determine whether he should be classed as, say, a chemist or a philosopher. The levels of categories that give a man satisfaction are usually determined by his genetic and personal experience before he is twenty and seldom change thereafter. When a category becomes recognized as an aggregate of the categories of the next lower level, one speaks of a *reduction of categories*. It is an empirical question whether all categories are reducible. At present there is no compelling evidence for the irreducibility of any category.

Scientific thought uses both induction and deduction combined into the hypothetico-deductive method. Operational concepts are recommended, but nonoperational concepts may be used if their employment permits successful predictions. At the basis of scientific thought lie certain unvalidated assumptions. These assumptions are metaphysical in the sense that they are not subject to direct empirical validation. The justification for these assumptions lies in the utility of science as a survival technique for man.

Chapter IV

Science and Mathematics

Counting. Coordinate systems. Functions. Hypernumbers. Vectors and displacements. Invariants. Products of hypernumbers. Quaternions and commutators. Matrices and tensors. Rank and dimension. Spinors. Statistics. Distributions. Probability. Thought experiments.

Mathematics originated as an abstraction from empirical experience of the external world. Language developed as our remote ancestors tried to convey to each other information needed for their common survival. The quantitative aspects of language constituted the beginning of mathematics. The information behind the phrases "Exit, pursued by a bear," and "Exit, pursued by bears," was often a matter of life or death to a cave man. The distinction between *one* and *more-than-one* is so vital that almost all languages have separate forms (singular and plural) to accentuate the difference, and some languages even have a third form (the dual) to be used when precisely two things are mentioned.

The operation of counting appeared when it was found that the same adjective, say *three*, could be used for a trio of fish, a trio of bears, or a trio of anything. This abstraction is only slightly more complicated than the discovery that the same adjective, say *red*, could be applied to blood, flowers, and berries. Number is a described property of a collection, but color may be a described appearance of single objects.

Later in man's development, it was noted that a trio of fish caught by father combined with a duo of fish caught by mother produced a quintet of fish when put together. Still later some genius noted that a trio of anything combined with a duo of anything produced a quintet of that anything: arithmetic was born. The tables of addition, subtraction, multiplication, and division constitute a compendium of experimentally observed facts.

Numbers are abstractions from the external world, but numbers themselves have properties. An integer such as 9 has exact divisors which are integers, 1, 3, and 9, but 7 has only 1 and 7 as integer divisors. An integer exactly divisible by only itself and one is called a *prime number*. The first few prime numbers are 1, 2, 3, 5, 7, 11. Thus the concept of *prime number* is, as it were, an abstraction of an abstraction. In such a fashion, mathematics, despite its ultimate origin in the physical world, soon becomes very remote from that world.

Arithmetic deals with specific numbers, as when we say, "Seven times eight is fifty-six." Algebra, on the other hand, frequently makes statements that are true about any number. This "any number" algebra talks about is assigned a symbol, say the letter x. If you wish to talk about two or more "any numbers," you assign further symbols, say y, z, and so on. Algebra then makes statements such as

$$(x + y)\,(x - y) = x^2 - y^2;$$

this statement written in the language of algebra may be translated into English as, "The sum of any two numbers multiplied by the difference of the two numbers is equal to the difference between the squares of the two numbers." This statement is true no matter what numerical value is represented by x and y; in other words the expression is true for *all* numbers. It is in this sense that one can say that arithmetic makes statements about specific numbers whereas algebra can make statements about all numbers.

Algebra also makes statements such as $y = x + 3$. Here you can choose any number you like for x, but once you have chosen it, there is only *one* value of y for which the statement is correct. If you specify that $x = 2$, then the statement is correct only if $y = 5$. Clearly, the value of y needed to make the statement $y = x + 3$ true depends on the value chosen for x. Mathematicians describe this situation by saying that y is a *function* of x. Of course you can choose y first, and then the appropriate value of x will depend on your choice of y. If y is a function of x, then x is also a function of y, and x and y are said to be *functionally related*. Actually, an expression such as $y = x + 3$ is a *propositional function*, which becomes a statement only when specific numbers are substituted for the variables x and y. We shall continue to refer to such expressions as "statements" with the understanding that the word refers to the actual statements that can be obtained by substitution.

A functional relationship between two quantities, say y and x, can be displayed pictorially (graphed) on a rectangular coordinate system. For each possible value of x on the horizontal axis, the corresponding value of y is located on the vertical axis. A line perpendicular to the vertical axis is drawn at the point y, and a line perpendicular to the horizontal axis is drawn at the point x. These two lines intersect at some point on the xy plane. The locus of these intersections is, in general, some kind of smooth curve which displays visually the functional relationship between y and x. Those who work with functional relationships can visualize the curve from the equation without actually plotting it. Thus $y = 3x^2 + 7$ would plot as a parabola, and $y = 3x + 7$ would plot as a straight line. If the equation has the form of $z = 3x + 7y$, then z is a function of two variables, x and y. A three-dimensional coordinate system is needed to display such a function, which appears as a surface in the x, y, z coordinate system.

Consider the statement $x^2 - 1 = 0$. This statement is true when $x = +1$

and when $x = -1$. The $+1$ and -1 are called the *roots* of the equation, and the equation itself is a *quadratic* because of the presence of the x-squared term. Extensive trials convince us that there are a great many quadratic equations with exactly two roots. Do all quadratic equations have two roots? We try the equation $x^2 + 1 = 0$, and are unable to find *any* ordinary numbers that satisfy it. The equations $x^2 + 4 = 0$, $x^2 + 9 = 0$, and so on also defy solution; no ordinary numbers can be found to satisfy them. Eventually there comes a very sophisticated idea. Let us assume that these equations themselves *define* a new kind of number that is not encountered directly in the physical world of everyday experience. These new numbers need symbols to represent them; we chose $+i$ and $-i$ to represent the roots of $x^2 + 1 = 0$, $+2i$ and $-2i$ for the roots of $x^2 + 4 = 0$, and so on. Clearly there will be just as many of these new numbers as there are positive and negative integers. Since $x^2 = -1$, it is seen that i is $\sqrt{-1}$, that is, the square root of -1.

The step described above was made in the sixteenth century. The new numbers were called *imaginary* numbers, a particularly unfortunate choice of name. It is true they are imaginary, but so are all numbers in the sense that they are abstractions made by the brain. We must not criticize too severely this unfortunate choice of nomenclature because the corresponding extension of the idea of number was a very remarkable and radical event, and it required three centuries before the matter could be seen in clear relation to the development of mathematics.

Were *imaginary* numbers discovered or invented? The current consensus regards such new developments as inventions satisfying a discovered need. These *imaginary* numbers provide a simple illustration of one way that new mathematical concepts come into use. It should be noted that *imaginary* numbers were invented to satisfy a purely mathematical need: there was no concern for any possible utility in describing the physical world. Since then physicists have found imaginary numbers very useful in describing the physical world, but such use is irrelevant to the mathematician. The mathematician as such concerns himself solely with the mathematical properties of mental constructs that have no obvious connection whatever with the external world. Mathematics cannot be independent of the external world because mathematics is the product of the human brain, which is itself made of matter and subject to all the laws describing the behavior of matter. Furthermore, the brain is constantly recording stimuli presumed to come from events in the external world. These two connections suggest that the operation of the brain will have considerable correspondence to the external world. The correspondence, however, is not necessarily complete. A mathematician probably can develop ideas that have no correspondence in the external world.

Arithmetic and ordinary algebra deal with the properties of ordinary numbers taken one at a time. It is also possible to deal with numbers in groups of two or three, or as many as one wishes. For example, one can deal with numbers two at a time, as in ordinary fractions. Fractions have more complicated rules of addition, subtraction, multiplication, and division than do single numbers (see Table IV-1). A group of numbers considered

Table IV-1

Hypernumbers	Corresponding algebra
Ordinary numbers 0, 1, 2, 3, . . .	Tables of addition and multiplication
Fractions $\frac{1}{2}, \frac{1}{3}, \frac{2}{3}$, etc.	$\frac{a}{b} + \frac{c}{d} = \frac{ad + bc}{bd}$
	$\frac{a}{b} \times \frac{c}{d} = \frac{ac}{bd}$
Complex numbers $(2, 3i)$ $(3, 4i)$	$(a, bi) + (c, di) = (a + c, [b + d]i)$ $(a, bi) \times (c, di) = (ac - bd, [ad + bc]i)$
2-Vectors $(A_x, A_y, 0_z)$ $(B_x, B_y, 0_z)$	$(A_x, A_y, 0_z) + (B_x, B_y, 0_z) = (A_x + B_x, A_y + B_y, 0_z + 0_z)$ $(A_x, A_y, 0_z) \times (B_x, B_y, 0_z) = (0_x, 0_y, A_xB_y - A_yB_x)$

as a single quantity is called a *hypernumber*, and individual numbers in the group are called *elements*. Fractions constitute a type of hypernumber with two elements. Each type of hypernumber has its own set of rules of combination called its *algebra*.

The concept of *hypernumber* is most useful in understanding the relationships between science and mathematics. Many of the quantities measured in physics are found to have the same properties as certain hypernumbers in mathematics. The following is a simple example of a system of hypernumbers. A farm expert describes each farm under consideration by a set of three numbers (a, b, c), where a is the number of acres, b the number of bulls, and c the number of cows. By adding the elements separately, he could obtain a hypernumber that represents his state, a being the number of acres of farmland in the state, b the total number of bulls, and c the total number of cows. The system is trivial and has no other interesting properties. There seems to be nothing in the farm situation to correspond to the product obtained by multiplying such hypernumbers.

When a carpenter asks for a "six-foot two-by-four," he is using a simple hypernumber that describes the board as being 6 feet long, 2 inches thick, and 4 inches wide. A railroad steam engine was once described as a "4-8-4" engine, meaning that the engine had four wheels under the leading truck, eight driving wheels, and four trailing wheels.

A type of hypernumber with two elements consists of the pairs made up of one ordinary number and one imaginary number; such a hypernumber is called a *complex number*, and the rules of combination of complex numbers constitute the *algebra of complex numbers*. Table IV-1 displays the rules of this algebra. Complex numbers are written as (a, bi) or $(a + bi)$, although the plus sign is misleading because it means something quite different from the plus sign in $3 + 4 = 7$.

Complex numbers were so useful that mathematicians tried to produce other new kinds of numbers by the same sort of process. Since the solutions of $x^2 + 1 = 0$ defined a new type of number, it was natural to try $x^3 + 1 = 0$, $x^4 + 1 = 0$, and so on. It was found that complex numbers were adequate to express the roots of such equations, and eventually it was proved that complex numbers could express the roots of any algebraic equation whatever. This proof led mathematicians to regard complex numbers as the more fundamental type of number and to regard an ordinary "real" number as a special kind of complex number having the "imaginary" part equal to zero.

Thus far in this chapter we have given specific examples of developments in mathematics. Now we can summarize the procedure in general terms.

Mathematics originated as an abstraction from empirical experience of the physical world. The symbols referred to actual real objects. Eventually it was found that the symbols and operations could be completely separated from any physical object, and systems were built out of the symbols and operations alone. The mathematician was then free to define any sort of symbol or operation he could imagine. Since symbols could be defined as having the property A, the statement "this symbol has property A" was true and could serve as a premise of a syllogism. By deduction it was possible to prove theorems that were true statements of the properties of the system of symbols. By this process an immense body of mathematical knowledge was constructed, a knowledge completely independent of the physical world except for whatever constraints were imposed by the fact that mathematicians themselves were parts of the physical world.

The scientific method is ultimately quantitative, and numbers are basic to precise observation and prediction. Scientists found that occasionally there was a one-to-one correspondence between the behavior of part of the physical world and the behavior of part of a specific mathematical system of symbols. They could then utilize the mathematical system as a model of that part of the physical world. The existence of such correspondences is not surprising since mathematics originated as an abstraction from nature, but the extent of a correspondence is unpredictable. A correspondence may predict accurately a group of events and fail completely outside that group. For example, the Bohr model predicted accurately the behavior of the hydrogen atom but was inaccurate when applied to heavier atoms. On the other hand, a correspondence may predict events not previously known, as the Bohr model predicted the ultraviolet emission of hydrogen. Every model builder hopes for such an occurrence, but often he must be content with less.

The scientist starts with a set of quantities he has measured in the external world. First he must find a hypernumber that corresponds to his quantities. In physics, for example, there are three basic quantities: mass, time, and length. All other measurements are combinations of these three. Mass is a property of a single object or aggregate—it is measured by an ordinary number. Time intervals and distance intervals (lengths) are properties of *two* points. Nevertheless they are also measured by ordinary numbers. Hypernumbers with one element, that is, ordinary numbers, are called *scalar numbers* and correspond to *scalar quantities* in the physical world.

After scalars, the next simplest quantity in the physical world is a *displacement*, a motion from one place to another. A displacement involves both direction and magnitude, and therefore requires a hypernumber with more than one element. Displacements in a plane require two elements or components, and the corresponding hypernumber is called a *2-vector*; displacements in three-dimensional space require three components and are called *3-vectors*. In general a displacement in *n*-dimensional space requires *n* components and is described by an *n*-vector. Many other physical quantities—forces, velocities, accelerations, etc.—are also described by vectors.

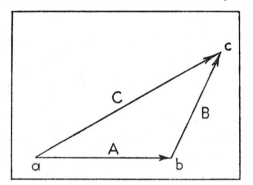

Figure IV-1. Addition of two displacements represented by vectors. If one walks from *a* to *b* and then from *b* to *c*, the resultant displacement is as though one had walked from *a* to *c* directly. This is expressed by saying that vector *A* plus vector *B* yields a resultant vector *C*.

The properties of vectors, which are invisible abstractions, can be visualized by a geometrical model as in Figure IV-1. This model illustrates 2-vectors; the properties of *n*-vectors are analogous. This figure is to be regarded as a map of a field. A person starts at *a* and walks to *b*. The displacement *ab* is represented by the arrow that has the proper direction and whose length *A* is related to the actual motion by the fixed scale factor of the map. The person then walks from *b* to *c*, a displacement represented by the arrow *B*. The person started at *a* and ended at *c*; he could have achieved the same resultant position by walking from *a* to *c* directly. Hence the vector *C* is called the *resultant* of *A* and *B*, and the process of following the displacement

A by the displacement B is called *vector addition*. It may seem an invitation to confusion to use a familiar word such as *addition* in this new way, but it will soon be seen that ordinary addition is a special case of this more general vector addition. One writes $C = A + B$ and specifies that A, B, C are vectors; this automatically implies that the sign $+$ means vector addition. Frequently a special type face (say, boldface or a German capital) is used to remind the reader that the quantities are vectors.

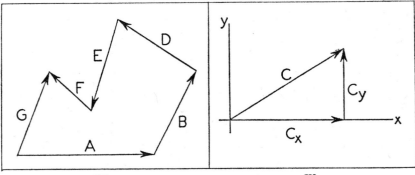

IV-2   IV-3

Figure IV-2. Addition of five displacement vectors. The resultant of the successive displacements A, B, D, E, F is the vector G. Vectors are added by this tail-on-head method: the resultant vector is from the tail of the first vector to the head of the last vector.

Figure IV-3. Components of a vector in a plane. The rectangular components of vector C are C_x along the x axis and C_y along the y axis. Note that vector C is the vector sum of vector C_x plus vector C_y.

Any number of vectors may be added by this tail-on-head method. In Figure IV-2 is shown an example of the addition $A + B + D + E + F = G$. The vector G is the resultant (or sum) of A, B, D, E, F and the vectors A, B, D, E, F are *components* of the vector G. Clearly, a general vector can be expressed as a vector sum of any specified number of components in many ways; the way that is useful will be suggested by the problem under consideration. The commonest method is to resolve a vector (like C in Figure IV-3) into two components C_x and C_y which are perpendicular to each other. Even this can be done in a large number of ways by rotating the x and y axes. It is easy to see that the same resultant occurs whether one adds vectors directly by the tail-on-head method or adds their components.

The plane vectors discussed above may be used to illustrate a most important concept, the idea of *invariance* under a change of axes. A quantity is said to be *invariant* under an operation if the quantity does not change during the operation. As an example we will consider the quantity "length-of-vector-*A*" and the operation "rotation-of-coordinate-system." Consider the vector *A* in Figure IV-4. It has the components A_x and A_y in the *x, y*

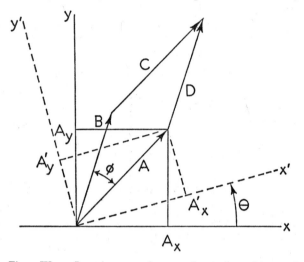

Figure IV-4. Invariance under transformation of axes. *A* new axis system *x'y'* (shown with broken lines) could be found by rotating through any angle θ. The components of any vector *A* change under rotation of axes, but the length of the vector *A* remains the same (invariant). Also invariant under rotation of axes are the angle ϕ between any two vectors *A* and *B*, and the area of the parallelogram *ABCD* which is specified by any two vectors *A* and *B*.

coordinate system. Imagine that there is a new coordinate system *x', y'* just like the old one except that it is rotated with respect to *x, y* through the angle θ. The components of *A* with respect to the new rotated position of the coordinates are A_x', A_y' since the vector *A* has remained fixed with respect to the paper during the change (or *transformation*) of the axes. If we consider two vectors *A* and *B*, the components of each change if one rotates the axes. There are, however, things that do not change when the axes are rotated. The length of *A*, the length of *B*, the angle ϕ between *A* and *B*, and the area of the parallelogram *ABCD* all remain constant when the axes are rotated: they are *invariant* under rotation of axes.

This idea of invariance is of the greatest importance to scientists. Consider that the vector *A* represents some physical measurement, say the displacement of a person. This displacement certainly does not depend on whether the observer happens to choose axes in the *x, y* position, the *x', y'* position, or any other position. Such a physical measurement must be *invariant* under a rotation of axes. This is a specific illustration of the fact that all physical measurements must be invariant under certain types of transformations of coordinates. Hence mathematicians' studies of the invariants of mathematical systems are of great interest to scientists because these invariants may sometimes be used for models of parts of the physical world.

We have concerned ourselves thus far with vectors in a plane—that is, two-dimensional vectors or 2-vectors. The vector concept is easily extended to three dimensions. Figure IV-5 illustrates a 3-vector A and its three com-

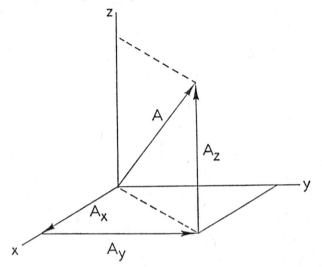

Figure IV-5. Components of a vector in three-dimensional space. The vector A is the vector sum of its three rectangular components A_x, A_y, A_z.

ponents on the rectangular axes system x, y, z. The same method extends directly to four or more dimensions, but 4-vectors are harder to visualize and usually handled by their components.

The multiplication of hypernumbers will be illustrated by considering the multiplication of a vector A by a vector B, as in Figure IV-6. The rectangular components of A are A_x and A_y, and the rectangular components of B are B_x and B_y. If one multiplies all the components in pairs, there results a set of four numbers A_xB_x, A_xB_y, A_yB_x, and A_yB_y called the *open product* of A and B. We have encountered a general property of hypernumbers: the multiplication of the elements of two hypernumbers produces another type of hypernumber with more elements than the original type. In particular, the open product of two 2-vectors produces a hypernumber with four elements which is called a *tensor*. Clearly, if the elements of a pair of tensors were multiplied together as above, a hypernumber with even more elements would result.

All the hypernumbers encountered by multiplication of vectors and their products behave in a similiar fashion under transformations of coordinates and constitute a family of related quantities. The family name is *tensor*, and each individual quantity is located in the family tree by specifying its rank and dimension. *Scalars* are tensors of rank zero, vectors are tensors of rank one, and so on. When tensors are multiplied, the rank of the product is the sum of the ranks of the factors. In the example above, the open product of two tensors of rank one produces a tensor of rank two. The number of components C of a tensor is given by $C = D^r$, where D is the dimensionality and r is the rank.

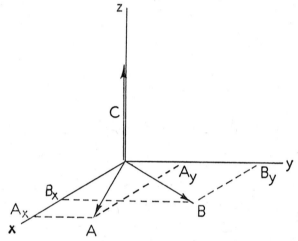

Figure IV-6. Multiplication of vectors. Vector C is the *vector product* of vectors A and B. The length of vector C is $A_xB_y - A_yB_x$ and the direction is perpendicular to the plane of A and B. The *scalar product* of vectors A and B is $A_xB_x + A_yB_y$. It is not shown on the diagram to emphasize that it is a scalar, not a vector.

The open product of two vectors is a second-rank tensor. However, in physics one encounters the definition, "*Work* equals force times parallel component of displacement." Force and displacement are vectors, but *work* is a scalar, not a second-rank tensor. Here is a clear need for another type of product. The need was satisfied by Josiah Willard Gibbs (1839–1903), who defined the "scalar product" of two vectors in 1881. For the case of Figure IV-6, the scalar product is $A_xB_x + A_yB_y$. This product is obtained from the elements of the open product by disregarding A_xB_y and A_yB_x and adding the other two elements A_xB_x and A_yB_y. The scalar product is a special case of an operation called *contraction* in tensor algebra. Contraction reduces the rank of a tensor by two. In this case the open product of two vectors (rank-one tensors) is a second-rank tensor, and contraction reduces the second-rank tensor to a zero-rank tensor or scalar.

In physics one also encounters the definition, "*torque* equals force times perpendicular component of displacement." Here force and displacement are vectors in a plane, and the *torque* is a vector perpendicular to the plane. Gibbs defined the "vector product" of two vectors to describe this situation. For the case of Figure IV-6, the product vector C has the length $A_x B_y - A_y B_x$ and is in the direction of the z axis. This product is obtained from the elements of the open product by disregarding $A_x B_x$ and $A_y B_y$ and combining the other two as indicated. The product "vector" obtained in this fashion is actually a very special case of a second-rank tensor which has only one independent element not equal to zero.

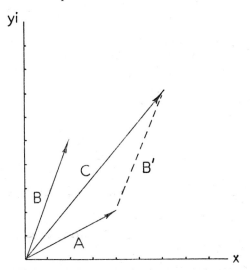

Figure IV-7. Addition of complex numbers. Complex number C is the sum of complex numbers A and B. The x component of vector C is the sum of the x components of vectors A and B, and the y component of vector C is the sum of the y components of vectors A and B. Vector C may also be obtained by moving B parallel to itself to position B', where the tail-on-head rule of vector addition can be used.

The properties of a complex number may be visualized by using a geometrical model in which the complex number is represented by a 2-vector in a special plane coordinate system. This model was invented independently by C. Wessel (1745–1818) in 1797 and by J. R. Argand (1768–1822) in 1806. Each complex number (a, bi) has a "real" part $(a, \quad)$ and an "imaginary" part $(\quad, bi)$. The Wessel-Argand diagram uses a plane rectangular coordinate system. The "real" part of the complex number is plotted along the x axis and the "imaginary" part is plotted along the y axis (see Figure IV-7). Each complex number is thereby represented by a single point in the *xy* plane. The vector drawn from the origin to the point just located also represents the complex number.

When complex numbers are added by adding their components, the vector model adds in the usual tail-on-head fashion as shown in Figure IV-7. When complex numbers are multiplied as though they were ordinary binomials, the product is another complex number with elements given by the expressions in Table IV-1. Note that complex numbers are very special hypernumbers in that their product does not yield a hypernumber of higher order. Note also that, when complex numbers are represented as vectors, the complex number product is different from both the vector product and scalar product of ordinary vector algebra. In Figure IV-8 the product

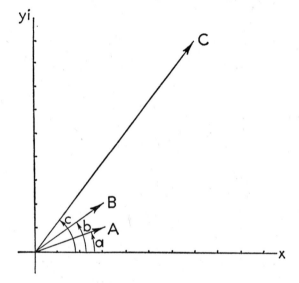

Figure IV-8. Multiplication of complex numbers. Complex number *C* is the product of complex numbers *A* and *B*. The length of vector *C* equals the product of the lengths of *A* and B. The angle *c* is the sum of angles *a* and *b*. The components of vector *C* may be computed from the components of *A* and B by using the rules of complex algebra given in Table IV-1.

vector *C* is in the same plane as vectors *A* and *B*, and the length of *C* equals the length of *A* multiplied by the length of *B*. The angle *c* equals the sum of angles *a* and *b*.

Complex numbers are used by electrical engineers for models of the quantities encountered when working with alternating currents. A hypernumber with two elements is needed, one element each for the magnitude and phase of the physical quantity concerned. The correspondence between complex numbers and alternating-current quantities is especially interesting because it is incomplete. When dealing with direct currents, one encounters the relationship, "Power equals voltage times amperage." The analogous expression for alternating currents would require that power (a scalar) depend on the product of two complex number vectors, but the ordinary algebra of complex numbers has only one product, which produces another complex number vector, not a scalar. The correspondence could be completed by defining a suitable "scalar product" for complex number algebra, but this step is not often taken.

One would expect there to be some system like complex numbers to correspond to 3-vectors. Sir William Rowan Hamilton (1805–1865) worked many years to construct such a system, and in 1843 he succeeded instead in developing a system that corresponded somewhat to 4-vectors. Hamilton's discovery was made suddenly, and is an excellent example of the "illumition" process described in Chapter XIV. Since then it has been proved that systems like complex numbers are possible only in spaces of one, two, or four dimensions. Hamilton's constructs were called *quaternions* because of their four components and are historically important because they were the first mathematical system constructed in which the algebraic law of commutation did not hold. The law of commutation says that, when multiplying quantities, the same answer results regardless of the order in which multiplication is performed. That is, in a commutative algebra, $A \times B$ is equal to $B \times A$. Quaternion algebra was the first of many noncommutative algebras, where $A \times B$ is not equal to $B \times A$. Such an occurrence is impossible with ordinary numbers or complex numbers, and direct experience with such algebras is needed to become convinced that noncommutability is not contrary to common sense.

Quaternions were invented before ordinary vectors were developed. Quaternions, however, were not easily applicable to the kind of models needed by nineteenth century physics and were not much used except by a few enthusiasts. About 1881 the vector aspect of quaternions was separated from the general system by Josiah Willard Gibbs and, with new symbols, was developed into the vector algebra of today. The full system of vector algebra is a very sophisticated branch of mathematics, but the basic aspects of vectors are now taught in the most elementary physics courses.

Any mathematical symbol can have two aspects; it can be regarded as a quantity, or it can be combined with a rule of operation and regarded as an *operator*. Thus the symbol "3" designates a quantity. From this "3" we can construct an operator [3+]. Then, when we write [3+] (2) = 5, we mean that the operation of adding 3 to 2 produces 5. We could write [3×] (2) = 6, which means that the operation of multiplying 3 by 2 produces 6. Other examples would be [√] (4) = 2, [−3 ×] (2) = −6, etc.

In Figure IV-9 the vector A is drawn on a coordinate system as shown with the tail of the vector at the origin. Clearly any positive number can be represented by a vector of appropriate length pointing to the right on the *x* axis. Negative numbers are similarly represented by vectors along the *x* axis that point toward the left. On Figure IV-9 vector A represents the number $(+3)$, and vector E represents the number (-2). Ordinary numerical addition is a special case of vector addition where the vectors have the

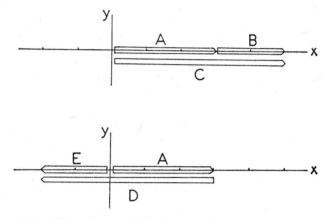

Figure IV-9. Geometrical model of scalar addition and subtraction. Scalars may be regarded as special vectors whose y components are zero. The scalar addition $3 + 2 = 5$ corresponds to the vector addition $A + B = C$. Scalar subtraction $3 - 5 = -2$ corresponds to the vector addition $A + D = E$ or $A - C = E$.

same direction. Thus $(+3) + (+2) = (+5)$ numerically corresponds to the vector addition $(A) + (B) = (C)$. Numerical subtraction corresponds to rotating a vector through 180 degrees before proceeding with vector summation. Thus

$$(+3) - (+5) = (+3) + (-5) = (-2)$$

numerically corresponds to $(A) + (D) = E$. The effect of rotation operators is shown in Figure IV-10.

In operator symbols, multiplication of vector A by the number (-1) is represented by $[-1 \times] (A) = -A$ and clearly rotates the vector 180 degrees counterclockwise. If we operate on $-A$ with $[-1 \times]$, we produce a second 180-degree rotation and again obtain the original vector A. This is a geometrical model of the statement that "minus one times minus one is plus one," which sometimes seems very strange to beginning algebra students.

The Wessel-Argand diagram (Figure IV-11) allows one to regard $[i \times]$ as a 90-degree rotation operator. The vector A along the x axis represents the real number A. Perform the operation $[i \times] (A) = Ai$. The result is a vector of length A along the y axis. The vector A has been rotated 90 degrees counterclockwise. Now rotate the vector Ai through 90 degrees by performing the operation $[i \times] (Ai) = -A$. This is a geometrical model of the statement that "i times i is minus one," or equivalently, that i is the square root of -1.

A quite general type of hypernumber is the *square matrix.* Following are

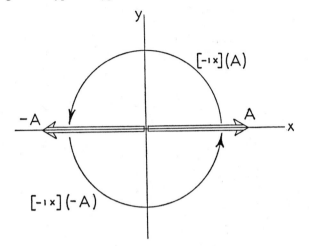

Figure IV-10. Rotation of vectors. The action of the operator $[-1 \times]$ on vector A rotates vector A by 180° into the vector $-A$. Application of the same operator on vector $-A$ rotates vector $-A$ by 180° into vector A. This is a geometrical model of $(-1) \times (-1) = (+1)$.

examples of 2×2, 3×3, and 4×4 square matrices, with 4, 9, and 16 elements respectively:

$$\begin{vmatrix} a_{11} & a_{12} \\ a_{21} & a_{22} \end{vmatrix}, \quad \begin{vmatrix} b_{11} & b_{12} & b_{13} \\ b_{21} & b_{22} & b_{23} \\ b_{31} & b_{32} & b_{33} \end{vmatrix}, \quad \begin{vmatrix} c_{11} & c_{12} & c_{13} & c_{14} \\ c_{21} & c_{22} & c_{23} & c_{24} \\ c_{31} & c_{32} & c_{33} & c_{34} \\ c_{41} & c_{42} & c_{43} & c_{44} \end{vmatrix}.$$

Note that the subscripts indicate the place of each element in the array. Each element may be real or complex. The matrix a_{ij}, for example, is a set of four numbers. This same array has a *single* number associated with it called the *determinant* of the matrix, which may be computed from the expression:

$$\det a_{ij} = a_{11}a_{22} - a_{21}a_{12}.$$

Matrices are multiplied by a rule that is illustrated for the special case of two 2×2 matrices:

$$\begin{vmatrix} A_{11} & A_{12} \\ A_{21} & A_{22} \end{vmatrix} \times \begin{vmatrix} B_{11} & B_{12} \\ B_{21} & B_{22} \end{vmatrix} = \begin{vmatrix} A_{11}B_{11} + A_{12}B_{21} & A_{11}B_{12} + A_{12}B_{22} \\ A_{21}B_{11} + A_{22}B_{21} & A_{21}B_{12} + A_{22}B_{22} \end{vmatrix}.$$

Note that the product of two 2×2 matrices is another 2×2 matrix.

The product of two complex numbers is another complex number, and the product of two quaternions is another quaternion. The vector product of two vectors yields another vector, but the open product of two vectors yields a second-rank tensor, and the scalar product of two vectors yields a scalar. The open product of two tensors yields another tensor of higher rank, and contraction of this product tensor yields another tensor of rank two less than the open product tensor.

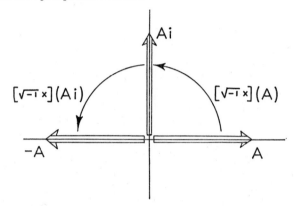

Figure IV-11. Rotation of complex number vectors. The action of operator $[\sqrt{-1}\times]$ on vector A rotates vector A by 90° into vector Ai. Application of the same operator on vector Ai rotates vector Ai by 90° into vector $-A$. This is a geometrical model of $(\sqrt{-1}) \times (\sqrt{-1}) = (-1)$.

If the elements of a square matrix transform according to the rules for transforming the elements of a tensor when the coordinate system is changed, the matrix will correspond directly to a second-rank tensor of appropriate dimensionality. Note, however, that the product of two matrices does not correspond directly to the product of the corresponding tensors.

Any complex number $(a + ib)$ may be written as a matrix in the form

$$\begin{vmatrix} a & b \\ -b & a \end{vmatrix}.$$

The multiplication of such matrices by the rules of matrix multiplication yields a product matrix which corresponds to the product defined for complex numbers.

There remains to be described a hypernumber of great importance in modern physics—the spinor. The mathematics of this quantity was first studied by Elie Cartan in 1913, and thoroughly developed by R. Brauer and H. Weyl in 1935. The corresponding physical quantity was encountered independently by several different theorists in the decade following 1927.

Spinors have rank and dimensionality like tensors. A 2-vector with real

Table IV-2

Physical quantity	Mathematical quantity	Components	Dimension	Rank
Mass	Scalar	1	1	0
A-c voltage	Complex number	2	2	1
Displacement:				
in 2-space	2-vector	2	2	1
in 3-space	3-vector	3	3	1
in 4-space	4-vector	4	4	1
Rotation:				
in 4-space	Quaternions	4	4	1
in 2-space	2×2 real matrix	4	2	2
in 3-space	3×3 real matrix	9	3	2
in 4-space	4×4 real matrix	16	4	2
Moment of inertia	2nd-rank 3-tensor	9	3	2
Momentum-energy	2nd-rank 4-tensor	16	4	2
Curvature of 4-space	4th-rank 4-tensor	256	4	4

numbers for components is a first-rank tensor in two-dimensional space. The open product of two first-rank tensors yields a second-rank tensor, and so on to higher ranks. A 2-vector with complex numbers for components is a first-rank spinor in two-dimensional space. The products of first-rank spinors are second-rank spinors, and so on.

A first-rank tensor may be visualized by a geometrical model—a directed line segment in a plane. A first-rank spinor may also be visualized, but the geometrical model is more elaborate since such a spinor has two complex numbers (four real numbers) for elements. It can be shown that there is a functional relationship between the four real number elements of a first-rank spinor and the four real numbers R, θ, ϕ, λ, shown in Figure IV-12. The angles θ and ϕ orient the vector, R specifies its length, and the angle λ specifies its plane of polarization. Each angle must range from 0 to 720 degrees for complete correspondence. This "polarized vector" in three-dimensional space may be used as a geometrical model of a first-rank spinor.

The algebra of spinors is even more elaborate than the algebra of tensors. There are some correspondences between these two types of hypernumbers. A certain type of second-rank spinor corresponds to a very special kind of second-rank tensor. Another type of second-rank spinor can be associated with a 4-vector. Zero-rank spinors correspond to scalars.

We have by now encountered a half-dozen different algebras. These and many others were developed during the past century. As it became clear that there was no limit to the number of possible algebras, mathematicians turned their attention from individual algebras to a study of the properties of algebras in general. The name of this field of study is a choice example of understatement—*abstract algebra*. Those who would "sail strange seas of thought, alone" are invited to explore this exotic mental world.

Statistics is that part of mathematics that makes quantitative predictions from the data provided by repeated events. These repeated events may be actual experimental repetitions as in error theory, or they may be imaginary repetitions as in the ensembles of statistical mechanics. Statistics provides a quantitative example of the scientific process usually described qualitatively

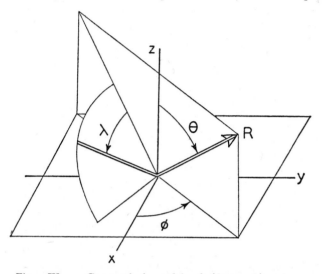

Figure IV-12. Geometrical model of (first-rank) spinor. Any pair of complex numbers may be written as a column vector, transformed by complex 2 × 2 matrices, and regarded as a (first-rank) spinor. Such a pair of complex numbers has four parameters which may be related to the four numbers R, θ, ϕ, λ. A first-rank spinor may therefore be represented by the polarized vector R, θ, ϕ, λ.

by saying that scientists observe nature, study the measurements, postulate models to predict new measurements, and validate the model by the success of prediction.

Consider, for example, that 100 measurements have been made in a single series of experiments of a specific physical quantity such as the velocity of light. The measurements range from 299.69 million meters per second to 299.91 million meters per second. The measurements are distributed over this range as follows: one measurement occurred in the interval between 299.69 and 299.71, two measurements fell in the interval from 299.71 to 299.73, and so on as displayed in Table IV-3. These data are graphed in Figure IV-13, and the stepped "curve" called a *distribution histogram* results. It has been found by experience in other cases that when more and more measurements are made and plotted using smaller and smaller intervals, the resulting histogram becomes more and more regular. It is assumed

Table IV-3

Distribution of 100 Measurements of the Velocity of Light

Velocity interval (megameters/second)		Number of measurements within interval
299.69 to 299.71		1
.71	.73	2
.73	.75	6
.75	.77	13
.77	.79	16
.79	.81	21
.81	.83	18
.83	.85	11
.85	.87	6
.87	.89	4
.89	.91	2

that, as the number of measurements are increased, the histogram will approach a smooth curve called the *distribution curve* for the data from the experiment. This distribution curve is assumed to be a fixed property of the particular set of conditions (apparatus, observers, weather, etc.) of the experiment. The curve is said to specify the *parent population* of results of the experiment, that is, the possible results obtainable from an infinite number of measurements under the conditions of the experiment. This curve is specified quantitatively by the parameters of its mathematical equation: the mean μ, the standard deviation σ, and others as needed. The mean μ is a number that locates the middle of the curve and σ is a number that tells the width of the curve; the exact shape of the curve depends on the experiment and the conditions. Certain common shapes have been named—for example, the *Gaussian* or *normal* distribution, the *binomial* distribution, the *Poisson* distribution, and scores of others. A particular curve is specified by its equation and its parameters.

In an actual experiment one does not make an infinite number of measurements but only a small number, say a hundred. This set of 100 measurements constitutes a *sample* from the parent population. The mean m and the standard deviation s of the sample are computed. These numbers constitute an *estimate* of the unknown parameters μ and σ of the parent population. Here is a quantitative example of the scientific procedure. The numbers m and s constitute a model of the unknown parameters μ and σ which describe one aspect of the external world. The parameters of the model are symbolized with English letters to emphasize that they are only estimated models of the unknown reality symbolized by the Greek letters.

In Figure IV-13 the distribution has a Gaussian shape. The mean of the sample is $m = 299.80$ million meters per second and the standard deviation $s = 0.04$ million meters per second. Note that an experiment which tends to reproduce nearly the same numbers has a small standard deviation, whereas an experiment which gives widely scattered numbers has a large standard deviation. The standard deviation s is half the width of the curve measured between the points of inflection.

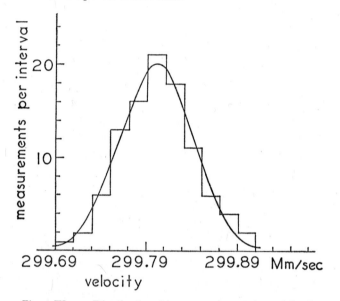

Figure IV-13. Distribution histogram (stepped curve) of 100 measurements of the velocity of light given by Table IV-3. The smooth curve is the Gaussian distribution curve computed for this sample. The mean is 299.80 megameters/sec and the standard deviation is 0.04 megameter/sec.

If one were to make 25 repetitions of the sample of 100, then there would be available 25 values of m, the mean of each sample. These 25 values could also be graphed and the standard deviation of this distribution of means could be found. This new curve would be much narrower, and its standard deviation would be about $s_m = 0.008$ million meters per second. When reporting experimentally determined values, it is customary to write them in the form 299.80 ± 0.008 million meters per second. The 299.80 is the mean of all observations and the 0.008 is the standard deviation of the mean, which indicates how much scatter there was in the numbers that were averaged to yield the mean value.

When the distribution curve of a sample of results from an experiment is known, it is sometimes convenient to be able to make a prediction about the next individual measurement. The area between the distribution curve and the horizontal axis is equal numerically to the number of measurements in the sample. In Figure IV-13 the area is 100 units because there were 100 measurements in the sample. If each ordinate of the distribution curve is divided by the number of measurements in the sample, a curve with a shape similar to the distribution curve will be obtained. This new curve is called the *probability curve* for the sample and is shown in Figure IV-14. The area between the probability curve and the horizontal axis is unity.

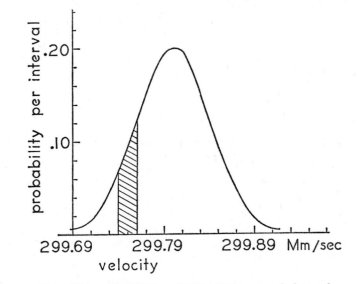

Figure IV-14. Probability distribution curve of data of Table IV-3. The area under the curve is unity. The area of the crosshatched region is the probability of obtaining a measurement between 299.74 and 299.76 from such a population.

The probability that the next measurement will lie in a particular range can be estimated from the area "under" the part of the probability curve that corresponds to that range. For example, the estimated probability that the 101st measurement of the velocity of light will lie in the range 299.74 to 299.76 million meters per second will be numerically equal to the area of the crosshatched region in Figure IV-14. The probability is about 0.06 for this example. The accuracy of the estimation increases with the size of the sample used to construct the probability curve, and becomes exact only when the sample consists of the entire parent population. The probability of 0.06 is interpreted to mean that if a very large number of additional single measurements were made, 6 per cent of them would fall in the region specified.

In some simple cases the distribution curve for data from an experiment not yet performed can be obtained from a "thought experiment" in which the result of the experiment for idealized conditions is imagined. For example, the histogram for successive throws of two dice can be obtained by assuming that the probability of occurrence of a specific result is equal to the ratio of the number of favorable results to the number of possible results. The probability of a "7" when throwing two dice is assumed to be 6/36, since there are 36 possible results when throwing two dice, and six of these possible results yield the required total of 7. At first sight this process appears to produce synthetic knowledge by a rationalistic procedure. On closer examination, however, it is seen that the ratio of favorable cases to total cases is a *postulated model* of the physical behavior of the dice. It is used extensively because it has been validated by a large amount of experimental results obtained with coins, dice, and playing cards.

Argument

Mathematics originated as a quantitative description of the external world, but it has become abstract and now concerns itself with conceptual operations upon symbols. The scientist can sometimes find or invent sets of mathematical symbols and operations that correspond to measurements obtained from the external world; he can then construct a mathematical model and make predictions. Hypernumbers and their algebras are especially useful because they can be chosen and developed to correspond to measurements of the external world. Geometrical models which permit one to visualize operations with certain hypernumbers are described.

Mathematical statistics provides an exceptionally clear example of the relationship between mathematics and the external world. The external world provides the experimentally measured distribution curve; mathematics provides the equation (the mathematical model) that corresponds to the empirical curve. The statistician may be guided by a thought experiment in finding the corresponding equation. The assumption that probability may be measured by the ratio of favorable cases to total cases is itself an assumed model for the behavior of the external world.

Chapter V

Factors Affecting Measurements

*Measurement as relationship. Motion of observer. Inertial system.
Restricted and general relativity. Riemannian space. Disturbance by
measurement. Quantum theory. Bohr model. Uncertainty principle.
Complementarity. Quantum mechanics. Current nuclear research.*

A measurement is a number that arises from the interaction of
an observer and his instruments with the object observed. The number so
obtained will depend on (1) the brain structure of the observer, (2) the
state of relative motion of the observer and the object observed, (3) the
physical and physiological receptors of the observer, (4) the interaction
between the observer and the object observed, (5) the properties of the
object observed, (6) the effect of the remainder of the universe.

When scientific measurements first began, the observer considered that he
was measuring a property of the object only. The early observers were either
unconscious of the effects of the other factors or considered that they would
be common to all human observers. It was not until the latter part of the
nineteenth century that scientists began to consider the effect of the observer
on physical measurements. These effects are usually small, and the accurate
measurements of the nineteenth century were needed to show their existence.
Consideration of the observer has led to the present division of physics into
two parts: *macrophysics*, which deals with the behavior of large objects like
planets and baseballs, and *microphysics*, which deals with the behavior of
small entities such as electrons and nuclei.

In macrophysics the motion of the observer must be considered because
such motion affects his measurements. He cannot avoid the issue by making
his measurements in a stationary laboratory, because, considered from the
sun, that laboratory itself is spinning through space at 18 miles per second,
which introduces a rather large effect. On the other hand, the act of observation does not measurably disturb objects having large mass. Mars is
observed by light from the sun that is reflected from the surface of Mars, but
this reflection does not disturb the orbit of Mars appreciably.

In microphysics not only the motion of the observer must be considered,
but also the effect of the act of observation upon the thing observed. When

an electron is observed by "reflecting" light from it, the electron is disturbed and its predictability decreased.

The *restricted theory of relativity* is concerned with the effect upon measurements of a constant velocity of the observer with respect to the object observed. The *general theory of relativity* is concerned with the effect upon measurements of an accelerated observer and the relationship between acceleration and gravitational forces. *Quantum mechanics* is concerned with the motion of particles of atomic size and smaller, when the quantization of energy becomes an important factor and the motion of the particle is affected by the mode of observation. These three models will be considered in order, but first the concept of a *coordinate* system must be introduced.

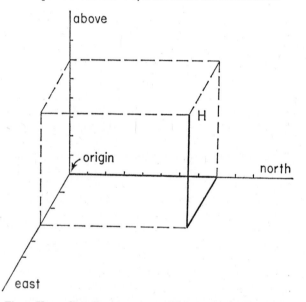

Figure V-1. Coordinate system. The position *H* can be specified by saying that *H* is 8 feet north, 3 feet east, and 6 feet above the chosen starting point, or origin.

A coordinate system is a method used for precise location of positions. First a starting position, the *origin*, must be adopted. If the origin is a mark on the pavement, then a man's hat can be located by saying that the hat is 8 feet north, 3 feet east, and 6 feet above the origin. These three numbers are the spatial coordinates of the hat. The origin might be chosen as a mark on the floor of a truck; then the driver's hat has coordinates independent of time, but a passing lamppost has coordinates that depend on time.

The restricted theory of relativity was advanced by Einstein in 1905; it rests on two basic postulates:

(1) The laws of physics are the same when inferred from the measurements of any two observers whose respective inertial systems are moving at constant velocity with respect to each other.

(2) The velocity of light in a vacuum is a constant independent of the direction of propagation or of the motion of source or observer.

In what sense are "the laws of physics the same?" The mathematical relationship between the position measurements made by two observers moving with constant relative velocity was first worked out by H. A. Lorentz (1853–1928) and has become known as the *Lorentz transformation*. Technically speaking, the first postulate requires that any equation embodying a proposed physical law be "invariant under the Lorentz transformation." That is, the two equations arrived at by these two observers will look alike and correspond exactly although the values of the quantities entering the equations at a particular instant of time will be different.

Each of these two observers, however, must make his measurements with respect to an "inertial system." A coordinate system is "inertial" when Newton's second postulate (which defines inertial mass) describes accurately the behavior of a free body moving under no forces. In short, an inertial system is one in which a free body moves, if at all, in a straight line at constant velocity.

Now for an example: suppose there is an observer G stationary on the ground. He experiments with a free body and discovers or invents a coordinate system in which the free body moves in a straight line. He then uses this coordinate system to describe the motion of a rocket. Another observer T is on a train moving at a constant velocity with respect to the ground. He also experiments with a free body and finds a coordinate system in which his free body moves in a straight line. He then uses this coordinate system to describe the motion of the same rocket. The first postulate of Einstein says that the equations of motion of the rocket as found by these two observers will look alike. This result is not trivial—if the train should accelerate by changing its speed or going around a curve, the two equations needed for the descriptions would *not* be alike.

Einstein's second postulate was suggested by the failure of all attempts to measure a change in the velocity of light with direction or with motion of source or observer. These attempts were made so persistently and failed so consistently that experimenters began to suspect a "conspiracy of nature" against them. Einstein realized that such a conspiracy was in itself a law of nature, and wrote it down as his second postulate.

This second postulate is related to the fact that the velocity of light (the only practical synchronization signal) can be measured only for a round trip. A one-way trip cannot be timed because it requires the synchronization of timers in different places, and this in turn requires a knowledge of the one-way velocity of light. The experimentalists are caught in a vicious circle. They cannot synchronize the timers and then move them apart because (as it appears below) such acceleration ruins the synchronization of the timers. The "conspiracy of nature" just mentioned has come back in a different guise. If an experimenter asks a silly question of nature, he gets a silly answer. Einstein recognized the silliness of the question in this way: it had been assumed that an absolute time existed such that any timers anywhere could be synchronized with it. Nature was pointing out most emphatically that such absolute time does not exist. We will see later that it is as nonsensical to expect in general to find the same "time" at two different places as it is to expect to find the same "point" at two different places.

Einstein's second postulate permits the definition of a kind of "simultaneity" at different places by accepting the arrival of a light signal as a definition of zero time. To "synchronize" watches on Mars, the earth, and the moon, respectively, a flash lamp is fired on the earth at zero on the earth timer. The timers on Mars and the moon are started at zero when the flash signal arrives. Any attempt to allow for the time of flight of the light signal gets one involved in a maze of circular reasoning.

From Einstein's two postulates one can derive mathematically five effects which have all been observed experimentally.

(1) The length of a moving body (say a high-velocity rocket ship) is shorter when measured by an observer on the ground than when measured by an observer on the rocket (Lorentz-Fitzgerald contraction).

(2) The time interval between two events on a moving body is greater when measured by an observer on the ground than when measured by an observer on the moving body (Time dilation).

(3) Velocities that approach the speed of light do not add as simple vectors, but require a more complicated process given by the "Einstein velocity addition theorem" (no object having mass can attain a velocity exceeding the speed of light).

(4) The mass of a body in motion is greater when measured by an observer on the ground than when measured by an observer moving with the body (mass increases with velocity).

(5) $E = mc^2$. Energy equals mass times the square of the velocity of light (energy has mass).

In brief, statements like the above hold for all physical quantities: kinetic energy, momentum, and so forth. The difference between the two observations would be negligibly small for a present-day rocket ship, but the difference would become larger as the relative velocity increased and approach infinity as the relative velocity approached the speed of light.

When the word "stationary" is used in relativity, it is merely a label for the coordinate system one chooses to consider as "stationary." There is, of course, no absolutely stationary system; one can only say that object or system A is stationary *with respect to* object or system B. In deduction (1) above, one can consider that the rocket is moving with respect to a "stationary" ground or that the ground is moving with respect to a "stationary" rocket. Suppose that there are two rockets, each containing an observer. Each observer measures the length of each rocket when they are stationary with respect to each other. These four measurements are found to be identical. Now suppose one rocket F is flying in a straight line at constant velocity with respect to the other rocket G, which is on the ground. Then observer G measures rocket F to be shorter than his own rocket G. On the other hand, observer F measures rocket G to be shorter than rocket F. These results seem to be contradictory only if one expects that the length of the rocket should be constant regardless of the conditions of measurement.

Consider now that one of the identical rockets mentioned above goes on a long, fast journey and returns, while the other remains on the ground. Such a journey requires a period of acceleration and deceleration, but nothing will be said about length measurements during these periods, and it is inferred that any changes of length during these periods will not persist to affect later measurements. The length measurements of the two observers agree when the two rockets are at rest with respect to each other, they disagree when the two are in relative motion at constant velocity, and they agree again when the relative motion ceases at the end of the journey. The contraction measured by either observer is deduced from the two postulates above by a careful conceptual experiment, and the consensus of theorists accepts the result. The contraction has not been measured directly, but such a contraction is in agreement with the null result of the Michelson-Morley experiment.

Although the length changes occurring during acceleration and deceleration do not persist, time interval changes during acceleration and deceleration do persist, and the accelerated clock runs slow compared to the unaccelerated clock. All periodic atomic processes are clocks in this sense, so it is inferred that living organisms, being made of atoms, would age more slowly in the accelerated system. That is, if one of a pair of previously identical twins went on an accelerated journey, the traveler would return younger than his stay-at-home brother. This was once considered a paradox because it appeared, if all aspects of motion are relative, that the traveler could claim that, from his viewpoint, it was the stay-at-home twin that had undergone the accelerated journey. The "paradox" was resolved by noting that acceleration is *not* relative, that there is a fundamental asymmetry between the two observers because the ground observer remained in a nearly inertial system while the traveler did not. There is now quite general agreement about this inference of asymmetric aging. This asymmetric aging is a prediction from a model, and an experimental check is not yet available. Considering that many other predictions of special relativity have been checked, it seems likely that asymmetric aging will also be encountered. However, it should be remembered that the postulates of relativity were introduced to predict the behavior of nature, and if the predictions are not correct, the postulates must be supplemented, modified, or replaced.

Asymmetric aging is not in contradiction with postulate (I) above because the traveling rocket does not constitute an inertial system, and the rockets are not moving with constant relative velocity. The traveler may return younger than his stay-at-home twin, but his mental processes have also been retarded so that his mental development is that of his twin when the twin was the traveler's present age. This "fountain of youth" has its price; the cost of eternal youth is eternal immaturity.

At present it is observed that velocities are relative and symmetric. Operationally one cannot tell whether *A* moves with respect to *B* or *B* moves with respect to *A*. If asymmetric aging is observed, then accelerations are *not* relative and symmetric. Operationally one can then distinguish that *A* is accelerating with respect to *B* and not vice versa.

Although the computation of time intervals for round trips requires further empirical data, the method of computation of time intervals on objects in motion at fairly constant velocity is well validated by experiments on the lifetime of the mu meson. About two microseconds after its creation in a nuclear reaction, the mu meson decays to an electron and a neutrino. This value of the lifetime is obtained when the mu meson is essentially at rest. Measurements of the lifetime of the mu meson when it is moving at high velocity give much greater values in good agreement with the quantitative predictions of relativity theory. From the standpoint of a laboratory observer, the time intervals on the high-velocity mu meson are dilated.

The increase of mass with velocity is a commonplace matter to those operating high-speed accelerators such as cyclotrons, betatrons, and linear accelerators. Energy has mass. If you have *E* joules of energy, you can compute its mass in kilograms by dividing the *E* by 9×10^{16}. In order to accelerate a particle you must provide it with energy. But this energy has mass, so you have also made the particle more massive. Any attempt to speed up a particle increases its mass, and eventually an impasse is reached when the additional energy supplies so much mass that there is hardly any increase in velocity. For this reason there is a limiting velocity for any particle having mass greater than zero, and this limiting velocity is 300 million meters per second.

The Lorentz-Fitzgerald contraction was first inferred from the Michelson-Morley experiment in 1887 and historically preceded Einstein's first postulate. We have here the usual procedure in which the theorist attempts to postulate a simple, general law from which an already observed effect can be inferred. When, as here, the postulates lead to several unexpected inferences that are later confirmed by experiment, the theory is considered to be successful.

Thus far the theory has been "restricted" in that it pertains to measurements made by an observer moving at constant velocity relative to the object observed. If either the observer or the object accelerates, then a more general theory is required. One might expect that the general theory would grow out of the restricted theory by direct generalization, but, in fact, the general theory of relativity developed out of a study of the problem of gravitational attraction. Later we will see that there is an intimate relation between accelerated motion and gravitation.

General relativity may be regarded as a solution of the "ether" problem. Many theorists had tried to invent a model that would throw some light on the mysterious action-at-a-distance of Newton's law of gravitational attraction. Most of these models involved the postulation of a peculiar substance called "the ether," which permeated all space and was invoked to explain action-at-a-distance. The explanations were not very convincing, and the physical properties required by the ether were so self-contradictory that the ether theories were constantly under suspicion.

Light traveled through the vacuum of space, and was regarded as a wave propagating through the ether. The ether was presumably at rest since it could hardly be imagined to travel along with all the diversely moving planets at once. If the earth, moving in its orbit, passed through this stationary ether and light was a wave in that ether, then the velocity of light ought to be different when measured along the orbital path or when crosswise to it. The Michelson-Morley experiment of 1887 found no such difference in velocity.

This situation and the equality between inertial mass and gravitational mass suggested to Einstein that the properties needed to predict gravitation should be assigned to space itself. The distinction between "space" and "ether" is largely semantic, but semantic overtones are as useful in science as in poetry, and the semantic overtones of the word "space" suggested several interesting ideas. In particular, it suggested that physical space might not obey Euclidian geometry. Mathematicians of the nineteenth century had invented all sorts of abstract mathematical "spaces" and studied their properties, that is, their geometries. Georg F. B. Riemann (1826–1866) specifically had studied a general kind of geometry that included Euclidian geometry as a special case, and Einstein chose to investigate the assumption that physical space might not follow Euclidian geometry. In particular he postulated a Riemannian space of four dimensions—the three dimensions of familiar space plus a fourth related to time. This procedure joined space and time into a four-dimensional unity called the *space-time continuum* and thereby led one to expect that different points would, in general, have different "times" also.

One can better grasp the properties of Riemannian space by considering conditions on a spherical surface. The surface of a sphere is a two-dimensional Riemannian space. Imagine a being who can comprehend only two dimensions. This Flatlander* has lived all his life on the surface of a big sphere, but he has lived in such a small area that the surface seems plane to him. He is quite sure that, if he should travel in a "straight line," he could go on

---

* This word was invented by Edwin A. Abbott (1838–1926) and used in his book *Flatland: A Romance of Many Dimensions*, reprinted by Dover publications in 1952 in paperback form.

forever unless he encountered the boundary of his space, and he finds himself quite unable to imagine such a boundary. When he measures a small triangle he finds that Pythagorean theorem is true: the square of the hypotenuse equals the sum of the squares of the other two sides within the accuracy of his measurements. When he measures the angles of his small right triangle, he finds they add up to 180 degrees.

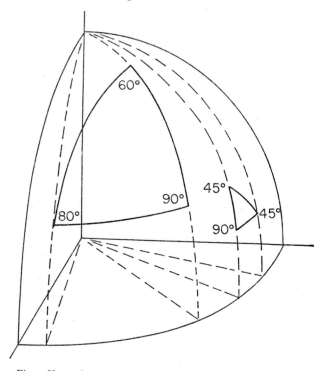

Figure V-2. On a spherical surface (a particular example of a two-dimensional Riemannian space), the angles of a small triangle add up to 180°, but the angles of a large triangle add up to more than 180°.

Now let us suppose this Flatlander becomes able to travel and to make measurements over large areas of space. If he attempts to travel in a "straight line forever," he finds that he can circumnavigate his space in any direction without encountering a boundary. Apparently his space is finite but has no boundaries; this baffles his imagination. Furthermore, the angles of his triangles add up to anything between 180 degrees and 540 degrees depending on the size of the triangle. The hypotenuse of a large right triangle as measured from actual triangles in his space deviates badly from the Pythagorean theorem.

About this time a Flatland mathematician was pondering the fact that length measurements seemed to come out "wrong" in the sense that the Pythagorean theorem did not hold for large triangles. It occurred to him that a Flatlander who actually was measuring a curved arc when he thought he was measuring a straight line would get the "wrong" answer if he used a theorem whose proof demanded straight lines. The lines along the sides of his big triangles were obviously straight to any Flatlander, so the mathematician postulated that his space itself was curved in some mysterious way that he could not see but could infer from his measurements. This "curvature of space" was nonsense, as any Flatlander could see, but the mathematician used the concept and succeeded in "predicting" the results already observed.

The extension of these ideas to our own space is clear. The Flatlander lived in a two-dimensional space of finite area although he could neither locate nor imagine a boundary. Our own space would accordingly have a finite volume, and we would be similarly puzzled by the lack of a boundary. The Flatlander inexplicably found he could circumnavigate his space by traveling in what seemed to him a "straight line"; our own space may have a similar property.

Here we find a need for a larger vocabulary. What appears to be a straight line in 2-space may be curved from the viewpoint of 3-space. Presumably the straight line of 3-space may be curved from the viewpoint of 4-space, and so on. We need a word for the "straightest" line, that is, the shortest distance between two points in a given space, and this word is *geodesic*. Thus the geodesic on a spherical surface is a great circle. To see how these ideas can be applied to the gravitational problem, we must first consider how Newton dealt with the situation.

In Newton's theory planetary motion is explained as follows. A moving planet moves "naturally" in a straight line at constant speed unless influenced by an applied force. Thus the earth deviates from a straight-line motion because of an attractive force from the sun. This attractive force is enough to pull the earth into a curved path around the sun, but not enough to pull the earth into collision.

In Einstein's theory, a moving planet moves "naturally" along a geodesic at constant velocity. The earth moves around the sun because the gravitational effect of the sun's mass has deformed space so that a geodesic has the shape of the elliptical orbit.

An ingenious (but somewhat misleading) analogy of space deformation has been invented. Imagine a tight sheet of rubber stretched horizontally like a drumhead. If several spheres of different masses are put down at random on the sheet, each sphere will depress the rubber sheet near it and lie at the bottom of a local valley. Neighboring spheres tend to roll down each other's valley, and thus appear to attract each other. The misleading aspect of this analogy is the necessity for a downward gravitational pull common to all the spheres. On the other hand, the space (the rubber sheet) is deformed in proportion to the mass of each sphere as in the actual theory.

Now we shall see how these ideas were introduced by considering the actual postulates of Einstein's general theory. These postulates include those of the restricted theory and also the following:

(1) At a single point of space it is impossible for an observer to distinguish whether a force is due to gravitational attraction or to his own accelerated motion (principle of equivalence).

(2) The path of a material particle acted upon only by gravitation and its own inertia is a geodesic. The shape of this geodesic depends upon the curvature of space which is determined by the gravitational field.

As an illustration of postulate (1), consider a man standing in an elevator stationary with respect to the ground and holding a box in his hand. The man feels a downward pull on the box owing to the gravitational pull of the earth below him. This pull he calls the *weight* of the box. When the elevator accelerates upward, the box feels heavier. If the man does not know that he is accelerating, he could conclude that the mass of the earth had somehow increased miraculously and thus was exerting a greater attraction on the box.

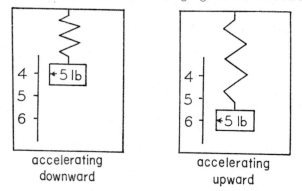

Figure V-3. The weight of a box as measured on a spring balance in an elevator changes if the elevator accelerates up or down.

Postulate (2) (Einstein's law of gravitation), which has been stated in words, is actually a deceptively simple-looking equation when written in tensor symbols. A tensor may be regarded as a generalization of a vector, and it is particularly suitable for the mathematical aspects of relativity because a tensor does not depend on the specific coordinate system in use. The components of a tensor change as the coordinate system is changed, but the magnitude and direction of the tensor remain constant. Postulate (2) contains Newton's law of gravitation as a special case.

From these two postulates one can derive mathematically the following inferences:

(1) A light ray that passes close to a massive object (such as the sun) will be bent toward it by an amount depending on the mass of the object.

The light travels along a geodesic, and the massive object distorts space in its vicinity. This effect has been observed during a total eclipse of the sun as a shift in the apparent position of stars whose light rays pass close to the sun.

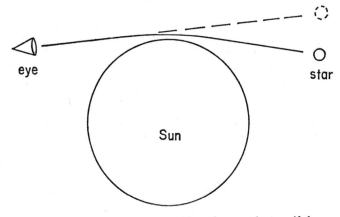

Figure V-4. The measured position of a star changes if the light ray from the star traverses a region of strong gravitational pull.

(2) Atomic processes in a gravitational field are slower than elsewhere by an amount depending on the strength of the field.

This effect is small and it was not until 1960 that a sufficiently sensitive apparatus was developed to permit the effect to be measured accurately. It was found that the measurement checked the prediction almost exactly.

(3) The orbit of the planet Mercury should deviate by 0.012 degrees per century from the position predicted by Newton's theory.

This 0.012-degree deviation had been observed before Einstein's theory was formulated, and the theory thus explained an already-known fact. This particular fact, however, was of no use to Einstein in constructing the theory because the mathematical computation of this number is much too complicated to be traced backward and its origin postulated *ad hoc.*

The general theory of relativity thus explains the gravitational field very accurately. It would be very satisfying if the electric and magnetic fields could also be derived from the same or similar considerations, but to date it has not been possible to do this satisfactorily, and the *unified field theory* remains the subject of current research.

We have seen the far-reaching effects on macrophysics introduced by consideration of the motion of the observer. Consideration of the effect on the system of the act of observation leads to equally important results in microphysics.

The first hint of things to come was found by Max Planck (1858–1947) in 1900. Experimentalists had studied the emission of light from a cavity in a glowing solid. As the solid was heated, its color changed from dull red through pale orange and yellow to a bluish white. Since this change was the same for all solids, it seemed that it could be explained without knowing much about the actual structure of any particular solid. Theorists were attracted to this situation like crows to a cornfield. Wilhelm Wien (1864–1928) derived an equation that worked fine for the bluish colors, but failed for the reddish hues. Lord Raleigh (1842–1919) and James Jeans (1877–1946) each derived a second equation that worked fine for the reddish colors and failed elsewhere. Planck derived a third equation that fitted the entire range, but only by making a postulate that seemed even to him to be practically nonsense. This postulate was:

(1) Radiant energy is not continuous but comes in particles. The energy content of a particle is equal to the frequency of the light multiplied by a constant number represented by the letter h.

The "frequency" of the light is a number that specifies the color the light will evoke if it strikes a human eye; the frequency of red light is about half that of blue light. Clearly these particles (called *quanta* by Planck and later called *photons*) are not all alike but differ in energy. The quantum of blue light has about twice as much energy as a quantum of red light.

This notion of quantized radiation received further support in 1905, when Einstein needed the same postulate in order to "predict" the behavior of electrons ejected from a metal surface by incident radiation.

Acceptance of this *quantum theory* was finally achieved through the success of a model of the hydrogen atom proposed by Niels Bohr in 1913. Hydrogen was the lightest, and, presumably, the simplest of all the fourscore different atoms then known. When hydrogen gas was sufficiently heated or excited electrically (as in a tubular advertising sign), it gave off a reddish glow. When examined through a spectroscope, this reddish glow turned out to be a mixture of a bright red line, a greenish-blue line, a blue line, and several others of various shades of violet. These lines had been known for nearly a century, but no one could imagine how a simple elementary atom like hydrogen could produce so much variety.

Bohr's model was based on the following postulates:

(1) The hydrogen atom consists of a massive, positively charged nucleus with a single, negatively charged electron moving like a planet in a circular orbit around the nucleus. The orbit may be computed from Newton's planetary theory by using electrical attraction in place of gravitational attraction.

(2) The electron may be in any one of a number of possible definite orbits. The possible orbits are those for which the angular momentum of the electron is an integral multiple of Planck's constant h divided by 2π.

(3) The electron does not radiate any light when it revolves in any one orbit, but it does radiate one photon when the electron makes a transition from a larger to a smaller orbit. The energy (and "color") of the photon depends on the transition—red for a transition from orbit three to orbit two, green for a transition from orbit four to orbit two, etc.

Note that this model provides no detailed picture of what happens when the electron makes a transition to a smaller orbit; the model gives only the end result, that a photon is emitted with a specific energy equal to the decrease in energy of the atom.

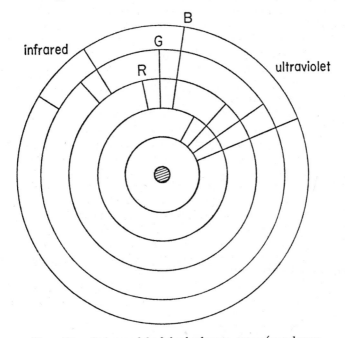

Figure V-5. Bohr model of the hydrogen atom (not drawn to scale). The circles represent some of the possible orbits of the single planetary electron around the central nucleus. The radial lines represent some possible changes of state of the electron. *R, G, B* show the transitions corresponding to red, green, and blue spectral lines of hydrogen.

The massive nucleus of Bohr's first postulate had been suggested in 1911 by Ernest Rutherford (1871–1937) on the basis of experimental results obtained by Geiger and Marsden in 1909. They had bombarded the atoms in a piece of platinum foil with the high-speed alpha particles that are emitted by radioactive materials such as radium. They found that some of these particles were deflected violently by the foil, thus indicating that the platinum atom must have a very hard and massive core. If you are firing machine guns at a pile of raisin buns and some of the bullets bounce backward, you will infer that the buns contain something harder than raisins.

This model "predicted" quantitatively all the then-known frequencies emitted by the excited hydrogen atom. In addition, it predicted others, some in the invisible region beyond the violet (ultraviolet) and others in the invisible region beyond red (infrared). When these spectrum lines were later found by instrumental means, the Bohr model was considered well established. Note that a particular hydrogen atom emits only one photon per transition, but that a tube of glowing hydrogen contains billions of atoms each contributing a photon corresponding to its particular change of orbits. The electron is normally in the smallest orbit, but can be moved to an outer orbit by heating or exciting the gas by electrical means. When the electron returns to an inner orbit, the appropriate photon is emitted.

These ideas were extended to the other atoms. Helium was pictured as a doubly charged nucleus with two electrons, lithium as a triple-charged nucleus with three electrons, and so on through the list of chemical elements. The Bohr model made accurate predictions for hydrogen and fairly accurate predictions for helium, but for lithium and heavier elements the model became less and less accurate. Attempts were made to modify the Bohr model (for example, by use of elliptical orbits) but it soon became clear that a more radical change was needed.

Planck had shown that light waves sometimes behave as if they were particles. One can visualize this by imagining the photon as a discrete group of waves. When a stone is dropped into a still pond, a circular group of waves spreads out from the central disturbance. If a narrow ditch opens into the pond, a narrow section of the circular waves will travel up the ditch acting very much like a particle moving along the water surface. Here we have a wave group acting like a particle.

In 1924 Louis de Broglie suggested that a particle might also have wave aspects. In particular he postulated a method to compute the "wave length" of an electron.

(1) The wave length of an electron moving at a specific velocity can be computed by dividing the Planck constant h by the momentum of the electron.

When light from a distant street lamp is viewed through an ordinary window screen, one sees a cross-shaped pattern of light. In 1927 Davisson and Germer "looked at" a beam of electrons reflected from a "window screen" made of the regular arrangement of atoms in a metal crystal. They observed a similar diffraction pattern, and the de Broglie wave length of the electron explained the effect quantitatively. Here we have an electron (previously considered a particle) acting like a wave. C. G. Darwin suggested that such things ought to be called *wavicles*.

When the wave aspect of the electron is applied to the electron in the Bohr model of hydrogen, a very interesting picture appears. The various possible orbits are just those for which an integral number of electron wave lengths will exactly fit the circumference of the orbit. The smallest orbit is one wave length in circumference, the next orbit is two wave lengths in circumference, and so on. Instead of picturing the electron as a particle traveling round and round the orbit, one pictures the electron as a wave spread simultaneously around the whole orbit and closed on itself. The electron, as it were, occupies the entire orbit simultaneously.

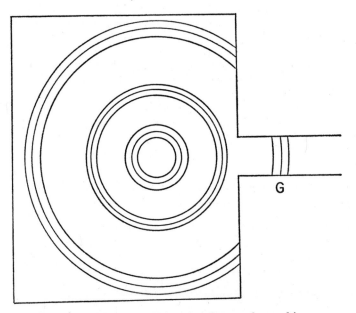

Figure V-6. Wave group. A series of stones dropped into a still pond produce circular waves spreading out from the center. The wave group *G* is a portion of the original circle. The group travels up the narrow channel and maintains its identity rather like a particle. (Reflections from the sides have been omitted.)

The wave length of the electron requires us to consider what we mean by "locating" the electron at a point. The electron may act like a particle, but it is also spread out like a wave. One can locate an octopus by giving the coordinates of his beak, but it would be unwise to forget that neighboring coordinates for two or three yards out in all directions have a considerable probability of being occupied by octopus at a given instant. Now imagine the octopus to be in a rather large dark room so that even his beak cannot be seen and located exactly; this is the situation of modern physics in trying to locate an electron or other small particle. One is forced to give up the notion of precise location and must accept statements such as: "The octopus is certainly somewhere in this room, but we don't know where, so we will say there is a probability that you will encounter him anywhere." In brief, the probability distribution of octopus fills the entire room. If there is a supply of octopus food in the center of the room, then the probability distribution may be more concentrated there.

Here we must consider just how an electron is located. The octopus can be located by using a flashlight—the light reflected from his surface locates him. When it reflects from his surface the light gives him a slight push, but he is so massive that he is not moved appreciably. We can also attempt to locate an electron by "reflecting" light from it, but in this case (since the electron has so little mass) the reflecting light kicks the electron violently to some other position. Furthermore, all attempts to compute just where it went have failed. The reflected light tells us where the electron was a moment ago, but now it is no longer there, and where it is or what it is doing cannot be computed exactly.

Many experiments have been designed to locate small objects (such as electrons) precisely, and all such designs have failed. This conspiracy of nature was cast into the form of a natural law by Werner Heisenberg in 1927 as the principle of indeterminacy:

(1) The range-of-uncertainty-of-position multiplied by the range-of-uncertainty-of-momentum cannot be smaller than Planck's constant h.

Loosely speaking, if you know precisely where a small object is, then you cannot know what it is doing; conversely, if you know precisely what it is doing, you cannot know where it is. In the Bohr model you know precisely the angular momentum of the electron in a given orbit, but you cannot know where it is momentarily in that given orbit.

This principle also applies to large objects, but then the uncertainty is so small that we are not concerned. The aim of classical mechanics (that is, mechanics before quantum theory) was to obtain an *equation of motion* which would specify exactly the position of a moving object for any given instant of time. Classical mechanics will not work for small objects like electrons; a new type of *quantum mechanics* has been develped since 1926 by Heisenberg, Schrödinger, and others to deal with small particles. In quantum mechanics one does not specify the position of an object as a function of time; one specifies instead a probability distribution as a function of time. A particle is located by saying, "At 3 seconds past noon this particle has a 33 per cent probability of being in this little volume, a 31 per cent probability of being in this adjacent little volume, . . . ," and so on throughout all of an extended region. This procedure sounds hopelessly vague, but it works beautifully.

Philosophers are divided on the interpretation of these known facts. One group says that if exact position is unmeasurable, one must conclude that the concept of exact position is not applicable to small objects; the other group says that mere unmeasurability does not disqualify a concept for fruitful use. Scientists, insofar as they are concerned only with predictability, need not take a stand on this question, but the pattern of future models and theory clearly depends on the theorists' attitude toward such matters.

In 1926 Schrödinger developed a theory of the behavior of electrons in atoms that has been very successful. As usual in such developments, it includes Bohr's model as a special case. The atom is described with a partial differential equation—the same type of equation for all atoms, but differing in its parts to correspond to each particular atom. The solutions of this equation describe the structure and properties of the electronic part of the atom accurately. For example, the solution for the unexcited hydrogen atom is a rather complicated function of spatial coordinates. When visualized, one gets a picture of a positively charged nucleus surrounded by a spherical probability distribution for the electron. That is, one is likely to encounter the electron anywhere within this spherical region. Whether the electron is actually spread out over this spherical volume or is fairly localized but moving about rapidly within the volume is a moot question. The general consensus favors the latter view.

When, in the Bohr picture, the electron goes from the smallest orbit to the next larger orbit, the spherical probability distribution gets larger in the Schrödinger picture. Furthermore the Schrödinger picture gives more details about the intermediate situations. The Schrödinger equation is definite about the emission of the photon for the reverse change, but the details of geometrical visualization remain to be developed.

In 1925 Heisenberg also developed a very successful theory of the atom using a completely different method. Almost immediately it was shown that the Heisenberg and Schrödinger procedures were equivalent, and now theorists use whichever is easiest for a particular problem. Heisenberg utilized matrix algebra for his mechanics instead of the differential equations which had been in common use since their invention by Newton and Leibniz. In ordinary arithmetic 4×6 is the same as 6×4; both are 24. In matrix algebra the order of multiplication affects the result; frequently the product $A \times B$ is not equal to $B \times A$. The difference between the two answers is very important in matrix algebra, and is called the *commutator*. In Heisenberg's theory the laws of nature appear as specifications of the value of the commutator for various pairs of quantities. For example, the commutator for the quantities describing position and momentum must be equal to the Planck constant h divided by 2π times the square root of -1.

Quantum mechanics can be applied to the motion of planets, but for large objects quantum mechanics yields the same results as classical mechanics. Any quantum mechanical equation to be completely general must be "invariant under the Lorentz transformation." This means that due consideration has been given to variation of mass with velocity and similar relativistic effects. In fact, the extreme accuracy of quantum mechanical predictions constitutes the most convincing evidence that the ideas of relativity must be contained in some form in all future theories.

What is the current situation in microphysics? Quantum mechanics has been so successful with the behavior of the electronic parts of the atom that it is also being used in attempts to construct a model of the nucleus of the atom. Currently the nucleus is studied mainly by throwing things at it and observing the splash. The things thrown are chiefly hydrogen nuclei or helium nuclei, and the throwing machines are the cyclotrons and other accelerators of the nuclear laboratories. The splash consists of large or small pieces of the nucleus. Much can be inferred from the mass, speed, and direction of these pieces.

Suppose we desire to study the carbon nucleus by bombarding a small piece of diamond with helium nuclei. The procedure may be compared to a study of the structure of watches by bombarding them with golf balls. On a scale in which a helium nucleus has the diameter of a golf ball, a carbon nucleus has the diameter of a watch. A small speck of diamond has many billion carbon atoms arranged in a regular pattern in space. The scale model should have many billion watches arranged in the same pattern with about a half-mile from each watch to its nearest neighbor. This analogy shows that it takes a lot of golf balls to hit a watch at all, and that the golf balls must have very high speed in order to knock a watch apart.

A watch may be regarded as having a dozen or so major parts arranged in a definite structure; the carbon atom also has 12 parts (6 protons and 6 neutrons) arranged in some structure. The pieces of watches that come flying off under bombardment by an energetic stream of golf balls are measured for mass, direction, and speed. From these results the scientist must infer the structure of the watch.

About fifteen hundred different nuclei have been studied so far, some of them made up of over two hundred protons and neutrons. Volumes of experimental results have been gathered and the situation with the nucleus in 1962 was very similar to that of the atomic electrons in 1910. The world awaits a new Bohr to develop a theory of the nucleus. This new theory, as usual, will include the successful parts of previous theories so that relativity and quantum mechanics will presumably be seen as special aspects of a more general concept.

Argument

A measurement is a number that arises from the interaction of an observer and his instruments with the object observed. A measurement depends on both object and observer, and is not a property of the object alone. When the object is subatomic in size, the act of observation disturbs it and special statistical methods are needed for prediction; these methods comprise the subject of *quantum mechanics*. When the velocity of an object approaches the speed of light—for example, a proton in an accelerator—special methods are needed for prediction; these methods comprise the subject of *restricted relativity*. The *general theory of relativity* considers the effects of accelerated axes and regards gravitation as arising from a deformation of space itself. All three of these models have been thoroughly validated by accurate prediction, but no single model that includes these three as special cases has yet been developed.

Chapter VI

Predictability in Science

Classical case. Quantum case. Causality and teleology. Functional dependence. Micro-structure of physics and history unknowable. Predictability in history. Macrostructure inadequate for philosophy.

The basic postulate of all science states that nature is, to some degree, predictable; this postulate is merely an inductive inference based on man's experience. He has found that attempts to predict have been successful enough to be useful in the struggle for survival. The postulate merely serves notice that man expects to continue the effort to make predictions as long as they are useful to him.

All predictions are statistical, but some predictions have such high probability that one tends to regard them as certain. Probability statements describe the degree of knowledge of a situation. The degree of knowledge may be low because (1) a measurement cannot be repeated, (2) repeated measurements yield different numbers, (3) suitable measurements would take too long, (4) measurements have not yet been made, and so on.

The empiricist observes that some aspects of nature are predictable with more accuracy than others. Some writers use the word *deterministic* in discussing predictability, but that word has metaphysical overtones implying a degree of knowledge to which the empiricist lays no claim. The empiricist seldom encounters any situation in which the word *deterministic* would be useful to him.

When men started to make measurements of the physical world, they first concerned themselves with objects visible to the unaided eye—stars, planets, cannon balls, pendulums, and other common, everyday objects. Later writers referred to this period of development as the "classic age" of physics by analogy to the classic age of Greece and Rome. Newtonian mechanics is an example of this "classical physics."

During the nineteenth century instruments were developed which permitted the measurement of objects of atomic size and smaller. The fact that energy is quantized does not affect measurably the behavior of the large objects considered by classical physics, but it does affect the behavior of atoms and smaller particles. It was necessary to modify some of the models of classical physics to predict correctly the behavior of such small objects.

The physics which concerned itself with measurements where quantization of energy is important came to be called "quantum physics."

It is commonly stated that the events described by classical physics are predictable, whereas the events described by quantum physics are not. However, such a statement exaggerates the difference between the two domains.

Consider a typical prediction of classical physics. A bullet is fired from a gun, and it is desired to predict how far the bullet will travel in three milliseconds. Here, of course, we are not interested in air resistance, gravity drop, moving axes, or any of the multitude of possible complications; we are concerned only with abstracting the simplest possible situation. The mathematical model for the simple situation is the formula $d = vt$, which tells us that the predicted distance d is to be found by multiplying the velocity v by the duration of flight t. In brief, the predicted distance (a single number) is to be obtained by multiplying two other single numbers.

We will assume that the number for t, the duration of flight, will be provided by a suitably accurate clock. The number for the velocity may be measured by photographing the moving bullet. Two very brief flashes of light a millisecond apart will provide a photograph showing the bullet in two positions; the distance between the positions provides the velocity in distance per millisecond.

We now have a single number for t, a single number for v, and their product yields a single number for d. But this prediction depends on one measurement each of v and t. Suppose that several observers have arranged their apparatus and made "simultaneous" measurements of v and t. It is known from experience that the various measurements of v, or t, or any quantity will not be identical. In fact, a large number of observations of the same event provides a *distribution* of numbers as described in Chapter IV.

In classical physics the results of measurements are not single numbers but distribution curves, and predictions from these curves yield other distribution curves. Classical physics assumed that the width of these distributions was due only to accidental errors of measurement, and that sufficiently clever design could reduce the width as much as desired. In practice one used the *mean* of each distribution, a single number, as the "result" of the measurement. From such mean values predictions were made of other mean values. The widths of the distribution curves entered the process only as an indication of the reliability of the prediction.

The corresponding situation in quantum physics is this: an electron is emitted from an "electron gun" and it is desired to predict how far the electron will travel in three milliseconds. The same experimental procedure is used as for the bullet. Again distribution curves are obtained, but these curves are much wider than for the bullet. It is inferred that the light waves used to "locate" the electron in the velocity measurement disturb the electron and change its velocity. Also, the electron is small, and the wave length of light used limits the accuracy of the experiment. Attempts to increase the accuracy of the experiment showed that increases in accuracy of location measurements always decreased the accuracy of velocity (momentum) measurements and vice versa. Such results are summed up in the *principle of uncertainty*.

We can now compare predictability in classical physics with predictability in quantum physics. In both regions the results of measurements are distribution curves, and prediction yields other distribution curves. In classical physics it was assumed that the width of the distribution could be reduced by more careful experiments. In quantum physics it is now realized that an increase of accuracy in position measurement is accompanied by a decrease in accuracy of momentum measurement and vice versa.

The *principle of uncertainty* describes the limitation on the degree of predictability of objects with small mass. Electrons, having the least mass of the fundamental particles, are most affected, and measurements of their position and momentum are most uncertain. Particles with larger mass (protons, mesons, nuclei, and atoms) are much less affected because the indeterminacy decreases with increasing mass. The position and motion of molecules and all larger aggregates are predictable with unmeasurably small uncertainty.

What happens if the behavior of a massive object, say a biological organism, depends on the motion of an electron? As an example, suppose the controls of a large truck are connected to a device whose control signals depend on the measurement of electrons from a radioactive nucleus. The truck will then simulate the measured behavior of the electrons. Whatever statistical behavior was characteristic of the electrons in that situation now describes the behavior of the truck. Science has no preconceived notions about the behavior of objects—whether they be electrons, biological organisms, or trucks. The behavior is measured and the appropriate statistical frequency curve adopted as a model. In some cases (as in classical physics) the frequency curve is narrow and is sufficiently approximated by a single number. In other cases the frequency curve is wide and asymmetric, and several parameters are required to specify the behavior.

The degree of regularity in nature has been described by a long series of models during the history of science. An early model was that of Aristotle, who observed that for the events of the physical world the past seemed to determine the present. The present motion of this stone was caused by the kick that was applied in the past. He termed this *causal behavior*. On the other hand, for the world of living things, the future seemed to determine the present. The planting of seeds by the farmer now in the spring seems to be instigated by the future event of reaping next fall. He termed this *teleological behavior*.

Later thinking about the teleological situation led to the recognition that it was not the reaping in the future which instigated the planting, but the memory of past harvests of previous years. The farmer is not motivated by the future, he merely extrapolates hopefully from past experience.

Aristotle was aware that causal behavior involved many causes for a single event. He listed four causes for each event, and later writers added a fifth. Aristotle's four causes were material, formal, efficient, and final. In the standard illustration, if the event is a statue, the material cause is the marble, the formal cause is the sculptor's mental picture of the form of the finished statue, the efficient cause is the action of the chisel, and the final cause is the purpose of the sculptor. Later writers added a "first cause"—the Creator of the sculptor. This list leaves out an innumerable collection of events just as necessary for the statue as those named: the quarry man who provided the marble, the geologic events which formed the marble, the drayman who moved it, the sculptor's mother, and so on without end. The causal model of the regularity in nature is not helpful for predictions because an event has too many "causes."

David Hume (1711–1776) discussed three aspects of causality: (1) temporal sequence, (2) contiguity, (3) necessary connection. *Temporal sequence* implied that the cause must precede the effect. *Contiguity* implied that the cause must in some sense "touch" the object which displayed the effect. *Necessary connection* implied that, once the cause had occurred, the effect must inevitably follow. Hume pointed out that *necessary connection* is an inductive inference from a large number of observed cases.

The concept of causality is an abstraction which has been used in an attempt to describe an aspect of all processes in nature. Empiricists have become dissatisfied with attempts to deal with this aspect of nature using the concept of causality and no longer use the word "causal" or its derivative forms. Empiricists use the concept of *functional dependence* to describe that aspect of nature previously referred to by the phrase *causal relationship*. The word *function* is here used exclusively in the technical mathematical sense described in Chapter IV, and none of the semantic overtones of its other uses must be permitted to affect the meaning of the phrase *functional dependence*. A quantity y is said to be functionally dependent upon x if, for each value of x, there is a unique value of y specified by some rule, graph, or table of values.

Consider that a man kicks a stone, and the stone is observed to move with a certain velocity.

Instead of saying that the force *causes* the change of velocity, the empiricist says that the change of velocity is functionally related to the force. This phraseology is merely descriptive and avoids any suggestion of necessity. Furthermore, the function chosen may ignore the time sequence if that is unknown or uninteresting, or the function may include a quantitative statement of the time lag. In Newton's second law (force equals rate of change of momentum) there is no indication whether the force precedes or follows the acceleration. It is implied that in most uses of the law the force and acceleration may be regarded as coexistent. The same situation occurs with Ohm's law—there is no indication whether the voltage precedes the current or vice versa. On the other hand, when an electric charge moves, the accompanying change in field propagates with the velocity of 300 million meters per second. The quantitative expression for the field intensity at a distance from the moving charge contains a "retarded time" which allows for the time of transit of the disturbance. The concept of *functional dependence* avoids expressing an opinion on Hume's aspect of *necessary connections;* the function may include or exclude the aspects of *temporal sequence* and *contiguity* as needed for description of the phenomena under consideration.

In present-day models of the atom, the behavior of the electrons is described by a probability density distribution. The details of the motion of the electrons are not amenable to precise measurements because of the interference of the measuring process. Nevertheless, many of the properties of an atom or of groups of atoms are predictable because such prediction does not require detailed knowledge of the motion of the electrons. The prediction of the behavior of groups of atoms does not require a detailed knowledge of the behavior of the constituent electrons.

There is a striking parallelism between models of the physical world and models of the social world. The microstructure of history is also unknown—not becuase it is unmeasurable but because the occurrence of the unique aspects of events can never be established with the same confidence as the repeatable aspects of events. It would be fairly easy to convince oneself that the supermarket served at least fifty customers during Monday afternoon. But complete conviction that the supermarket served a certain customer, John Specific Smith, is almost impossible with even the most elaborate preparation. Photographs can be faked, impostors hired, witnesses bribed, illusions induced; the universe seems to conspire to prevent conviction of knowledge of a unique event. If the course of history is to be predicted, the model used must be insensitive to the vagaries of individual events. Hitler's behavior to a specific Jew in a specific instance may be essentially unpredictable, but Hitler's time average of behavior to many Jews is a product of his heredity and experience and may be predicted by extrapolation with considerable accuracy. Similarly, the future of Africa cannot be inferred from single events or the behavior of one leader. Only when typical events repeat and a pattern appears can we extrapolate toward the future. It seems clear that, when models are built to make postdictions and predictions in history, only the repeatable aspects of events can be used as categories.

Although detailed knowledge of the behavior of electrons in atoms is not necessary for many kinds of prediction, the historical efforts to obtain such knowledge and the eventual recognition that such knowledge is unavailable have influenced profoundly the philosophy of science. Until the present century, philosophers attempted to construct their systems from a knowledge of only the macroscopic world because no other knowledge was available to them. If the atomic world was considered at all, it was tacitly assumed that its laws were essentially the same as those of the macroscopic world. The sensitive instruments of this century have made possible measurements of an extensive part of our universe that was completely closed to man in previous centuries. Furthermore, the laws of this new realm have turned out to be unimaginably different from the laws of the world of everyday life. The rapid development of electronics spurred by the great wars of this century has thus indirectly reshaped the philosophy of science in a way undreamed of by rationalist philosophers.

The new shape of the philosophy of science has made it inaccessible to those who do not read the language of mathematics. Philosophers of the past were often literary scholars versed in the great thinkers of bygone centuries. These men can now be read for inspiration and example, but their actual systems are obsolete, for they were based only on everyday experience and omitted the then undiscovered world of atomic phenomena. We must expect that the thinkers of the future will hold a similarly cavalier attitude toward our own extensive ignorance.

The empiricist sees no advantage to be gained in trying to classify a philosophy as materialistic or nonmaterialistic. These words, however, are still used by some other writers, and it is important to dispel the erroneous impression they often produce.

Scientific thought today is materialistic in the sense that models represent fundamental material particles or their aggregates and their mathematically described properties. The electromagnetic field in space may be regarded as an aspect of charged particles in motion, or the charged particles may be regarded as an aspect of the field. Either way the fundamental particle is intimately associated with the model. All measurable quantities are regarded as properties of matter or of the fields which are another aspect of matter.

The understanding of scientific writings is complicated by the fact that each noun in science has a double reference. When the word *atom* is used, sometimes it refers to the conceptual model of the atom, other times it refers to the "thing-out-there," the postulated real entity which the model attempts to represent. The entity itself has class one (real) existence, the model has class two (mental) existence. Writers on statistics in a similar situation have solved the problem neatly. They use English letters (m, s, etc.) for the parameters of their model, and the corresponding Greek letters (μ, σ, etc.) for the assumed parameters of the parent population. A corresponding usage in writings on the philosophy of science would lead to sentences such as, "The Bohr atom was the first successful model of the hydrogen $\alpha\tau\omega\mu$." I will assume it is not necessary to go to such lengths to be precise, and expect the reader to distinguish the cases himself. In this discussion on the materialism of the scientist, the reader will have to be nimble to keep the two references separate.

The rumor is current that scientists are "abandoning materialism," which, of course, is nonsense as regards their technical work. It perhaps arose when physicists began to regard matter and energy as two aspects of the same thing. The general reader understands technical statements in terms of his intuitive feeling for the words used. Hence he reasons: "So matter and energy are the same! But energy is obviously a highly unmaterial stuff. Hence I conclude that physicists have found that matter is an illusion and have abandoned materialism."

From the viewpoint of the scientist, a materialist is one whose basic models are made of fundamental particles and their aggregates: nuclei, atoms, molecules, compounds, and cells. Until confronted by an impasse (and none is yet well established), he will expect to continue to build successful models using such particles, their arrangements, and their forces of interaction. The fact that fundamental particles have aspects which are very unmaterial in the intuitive sense is quite irrelevant.

Sir Arthur Eddington is often cited as an example of a physicist who seems not to have been a materialist. He was a member of the Society of Friends, a believer in spiritual guidance; he also wrote witty passages about the unreality of his table. Surely this man was no materialist! But an examination of his writings shows that he was a materialist in his work in physics. His papers abound with symbols representing fundamental particles and their aggregates. The reader must learn to distinguish the materialism present in a man's technical writing and thinking from the idealistic and mystical doctrines that man may believe and practice outside his technical work. A scientist does not have to use the same categories in his work and in his life, but, if he does not, he must be content to exist as a dual personality.

Argument

The basic postulate of science is that nature is predictable. Both classical and quantum physics are statistically predictable. In each case measurements yield probability distributions, and from these other probability distributions may be predicted. For a massive object (the classical case) the width of these distributions can be reduced by careful measurements until the inaccuracy of prediction is negligible. For an object of atomic mass or smaller (the quantum case), the width of the distribution cannot be arbitrarily reduced, and the inaccuracy of prediction is not negligible. Accurate prediction of the instantaneous behavior of objects of subatomic mass, however, is seldom needed because our concern is usually with relatively large objects or properties which depend on the average behavior of many atoms, and these are predictable with sufficient accuracy. The situation with regard to history is very similar: the microevents of history are seldom known convincingly, but the broad changes described by macrohistory do not require an exact knowledge of the microsituation.

The aspect of nature that was at first described using the concept of *cause and effect* is now described by use of the concept of *functional dependence*. Modern philosophy of science must include the facts of modern physics and therefore involves sophisticated mathematics. Modern physics is basically materialistic because the fields that are characteristic of current models are aspects of the fundamental particles of matter.

Chapter VII

Physical Factors
Affecting Models

Research cycle. Parameters of electromagnetic waves. Triangulation.
Concept of space. Cepheid variables. Stellar spectra. Doppler effect.
Expanding universe. Information theory. Noise. Entropy. Maxwell
demon.

Many factors contribute to the models of nature that scientists construct. It is important to examine closely this process of model building, and to invent some way by which all conceivable factors will be brought to our attention. Figure VII-1, an idea flow sheet of the scientific method, is such an attempt to display the factors influencing models. It is called the *research cycle* to emphasize the fact that the feedback from the output (the model, M) to the input (the physiological receptors, R) is modulated by the physical and social world in such a way that the process of model construction is self-correcting.

It should be noted that the process can be regarded from a purely behavioristic attitude, with the signals which activate the physiological receptors as stimuli and the published model as response. Undoubtedly the part of the process which occurs between the physiological receptors and the published model includes factors which shape, limit, or even contribute to the model so that it is desirable to trace the flow through this region as well as possible.

This chapter and the next two attempt to indicate some of the factors affecting models by using the research cycle as an outline. The exact effect of the various factors remains to be determined empirically. The discussion here is designed only to draw attention to the factors, to try to imagine the effect of some of them, and to direct the reader to the field of effort where the matter is under study.

As an example of the use of the research cycle, let us consider a particular instance of an astronomer studying a star. A star P emits a light wave PC_1 which travels through space and is incident on a spectrograph PA_1, which analyzes the light into a spectrum and records on a photographic plate. This plate is examined by an experimenter using a light wave PC_2 which is incident on the retina R of the observer and gives rise to a pattern of nerve impulses N which reach the brain B and are filed.

Previously other individuals S have written books SA_1 which are read and give rise to signal patterns SC_2 which affect the retina R and, through nerves N, reach the brain B and are filed.

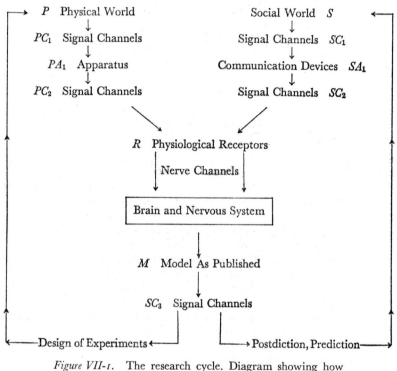

Figure VII-1. The research cycle. Diagram showing how feedback from the physical and social world provides a self-correcting system for the production of models which have correspondences to the external world.

The arrival of a problem signal from either P or S activates the brain to a scanning search of its files, which continues until the problem is solved or later signals relax the search. This search process turns up idealized parts of the original data (abstractions), and some of these abstractions are used as basic categories to construct a model M.

Model M is described in a scientific journal SC_3 and predictions are made. These predictions either refer back to the physical world P as designs for new experiments or refer back to the social world S of other individuals, who compare them to their stored records of physical data and emit signals SC_1

of praise or blame. By either route there is a feedback of influence which reshapes the model M and the cycle repeats.

Model M eventually comes to have a one-to-one correspondence with parts of the physical world P, but one cannot infer any further resemblance between M and P.

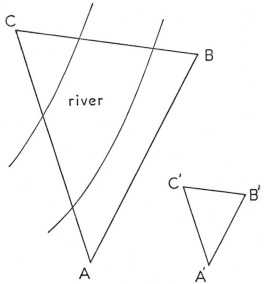

Figure VII-2. Triangulation. The distance from A to an inaccessible point C can be obtained by measuring the length AB with a tape, the angle BAC with a transit located at A, and the angle ABC with a transit located at B. Draw triangle $A'B'C'$, which is similar to triangle ABC, and measure length $A'C'$ with a ruler. The length AC can be computed from the proportion $AC/A'C' = AB/A'B'$.

Let us examine signal channel PC_1, the light wave from the star. An electromagnetic wave can convey information in the following ways: (1) direction, (2) intensity, (3) frequency, (4) polarization, (5) coherence. All of these can vary with time, that is, be modulated. We will assume for the moment that the wave is not changed by its passage through space although there is ample opportunity for any of its five parameters to be changed there. Hence the received signal can be attributed to the properties of the assumed origin of the signal, the star.

From the variation of the direction of the signal beam, a model has been constructed which attributes most of the changes in direction to movements of the earth and the solar system and only a little to the proper motion of the star. What is actually seen through a telescope is a diffraction pattern which depends on the construction of the telescope; the inference that a star is a glowing sphere of matter is based on its presumed resemblance to the sun, as indicated by its pattern of frequencies, that is, its *spectrum*.

The distance of a star is an inference of high order. Distances to inaccessible points on earth are measured by *triangulation*. Consider the inaccessible point C on Figure VII-2. A base line AB is measured off on accessible ground. Angles A and B are measured. A scale map of the situation is then drawn with base line $A'B'$, for example, one-thousandth of the actual distance on the ground. Plotting angles A and B on the map produces the intersection at C'. The length of $A'C'$ then is measured on the map, and this, multiplied by 1000, is the actual distance AC.

The longest possible base line on earth is its diameter. Such a base line was used to triangulate the distance to the sun. The earth moves around its nearly circular orbit in a year. The diameter of the earth's orbit (obtained from the solar distance just measured) allows one to triangulate to the nearer stars.

It must be remembered that the concept of space itself is a category or elementary model used to correlate and predict external stimuli. Since everyone as a child was led by parental behavior to abstract and use the category of space, it is regarded by most as an aspect of the "real" world. The space of the astronomer is very similar to the "real" space of childhood because both are inferences from triangulation. The action of the two eyes in estimating angles from the opposite ends of their 3-inch base line yields by triangulation the *distance* aspect of space. The motion of the eyes and head to receive incoming light rays yields the *directional* aspect of space. The size of the image of familiar objects on the retina yields auxiliary distance estimates.

The image on the retina is two-dimensional, and this fact combined with the concept of distance yields the three dimensions of our naïve concept of space. Our linear time experience yields the additional dimension of time. It is a moot question whether nature is intrinsically three-plus-one dimensional. Our use of this model may be the result of our early training, the arrangement of our sensory equipment, or some basic structure of the brain. Eddington and Synge point out that the $3 + 1$ model is forced upon us by the "common sense" of our causal experience. It must be remembered that "common sense" is what was learned in childhood. The $3 + 1$ model seems fairly adequate, and any other model must compete by providing better predictions.

The measurement of distance to farther stars depends on measurement of intensity variations. Certain stars called *Cepheid variables* show a regular change in intensity with a period of some days. A study of Cepheid variables whose distance has been triangulated shows that there is a functional relationship between the absolute brightness of the star and its period. Thus the absolute brightness of Cepheid variables can be found by measuring the period. Cepheid variables have been found in other galaxies; from their observed periods their absolute brightness is known. A comparison of their observed brightness with their absolute brightness permits their distance to be estimated. By this means it has been found that even the nearest galaxy is about two million light-years distance.

From the variations of intensity of stars with time, one can infer that some "stars" are double, that is, they consist of a pair of stars revolving around their common center of mass. Inferences can also be made about the dynamical behavior of the star; the Cepheid variables, for example, are postulated to be masses of pulsating gas.

The most detailed information about the star is conveyed by the *frequency spectrum*, that is, the variation of intensity as a function of frequency. When the light from the star is passed through a glass prism, it is separated into its component frequencies which are displayed as a *spectrum*. The pattern of lines and bands in such spectra has been studied in the laboratory, and it is known that each chemical element and compound emits its own unique pattern. Hence it has been possible to tell what chemical elements and compounds are present in the light-emitting part of the star. Our sun has such a pattern, and this fact allows the inference that the stars are similar to the sun. It has been possible to assign a temperature to each star as indicated by the kind of atoms and molecules contributing to the spectrum. From such measurements a model of the temporal evolution of a star has been constructed which describes its career from its formation to its final condition.

The spectrum pattern of some stars is shifted with respect to the same pattern obtained from a source in the laboratory. This frequency shift is called the *Doppler effect* and indicates that the star is moving toward or away from the observer depending on the direction of the shift. The acoustic analogue of the effect is familiar to all: the pitch (frequency) of an approaching sound source, say an auto horn, is higher than when it is receding. The change in frequency is proportional to the velocity. It has been observed that the spectrum pattern of a star in a distant galaxy is shifted toward the red end of the spectrum, and that the greater the distance of the star, the greater the *red-shift*. From this observation comes the inference of the *expanding universe*, that the galaxies may be flying apart as from an explosion. A second inference is possible: the farther away the star is, the longer ago the light left that star. Perhaps in that time long ago the atoms which emitted the light were different from the atoms of today. This model suggests a slow change in atomic forces with time. A third inference suggests that light which has traveled a long time through space may have undergone a slow change in frequency. At present there is no operational method to decide among these models. The expanding universe model is favored because the Einstein gravitational theory leads to a model of a universe which is unstable—it will either expand or contract.

The polarization of the beam has given less information than the previous parameters, partly because the measurements to date have been relatively crude. Inferences have been made, however, concerning the magnetic fields present in sunspots and in interstellar space.

The coherence of the beam (that is, the phase relationships of its component rays) has permitted the measurement of the diameter of some near stars by an interferometric method developed by Michelson. In this method the diffraction pattern of the star is formed only from two separated beams. The pattern then shows dark and bright lines (*fringes*), and the presence or absence of these fringes together with the separation of the beams and the distance of the star permits a calculation of the diameter of the star.

The preceding paragraphs illustrate the sort of information about the physical world which may be conveyed by a beam of electromagnetic radiation. A radio station conveys information by modulation of a beam of electromagnetic radiation. In the last twenty years investigators have been studying the basic laws of transfer of information. This study has become a field of effort of great importance and has received a specific name: *information theory*.

Information is defined as an *addition to knowledge*. If you are standing in the rain and someone tells you, "It is raining," you have received no addition to your knowledge, and the information content of the message is zero. On the other hand, if you are indoors and do not know about the weather, the same message *does* convey information, unless you do not understand the language. It is clear that the information content of a message must depend on at least two things—the message itself and the state of knowledge of the person receiving the message.

In order to attach a quantitative measure to information, it is necessary to consider first the basic limiting factor in the transfer. By analogy, if you wish to study what goods arrive in a city by railroad, the number of railroad cars arriving must first be considered. The number of cars arriving controls the flow of goods by setting a maximum to the influx. Some cars may arrive empty; if so, the railroad is not being used at maximum efficiency. At the beginning it will be well to see if laws can be established without specifying what goods, if any, the railroad cars contain. This first form of the theory will give an upper limit to the flow of goods even though the goods themselves are not yet specified.

Information theory, as currently under development by communication scientists, studies the transfer of messages without regard for their semantic content. This procedure permits a study of the limitations upon the process before the semantic problems are considered. Communications engineers were the first to study the subject, so that it is to be expected that research has concentrated on the situation where one person is sending a message to another person. The problem of the flow of information from nature to man has yet to be explored. It is likely that many of the results regarding man-to-man communication will be useful in this latter effort. The following paragraphs are illustrative of the approach used in information theory.

We have seen that the information content of a message depends not only on the message but on the state of knowledge of the person receiving it. Probability is a number which depends not only on an event but on a person's knowledge of the event. For example, if 52 playing cards are laid out face down on a glass table, then, for an observer above the table, the probability that the first card is an ace is $\frac{4}{52}$ while for an observer under the table the probability of the same event is o or 1. From the similarity of these quantities, one would expect that probabilities would be useful for a quantitative definition of information.

A well-known piece of information was transferred at Boston in 1775.

> ". . . If the British march,
> By land or sea from the town tonight,
> Hang a lantern aloft in the belfry arch
> Of the North Church tower as a signal light,—
> One, if by land, and two if by sea;
> And I on the opposite shore will be."

Before the signal comes, Paul Revere's knowledge of the event "coming by sea" is expressed by some probability P_b. If the two possibilities are equally likely, then $P_b = 0.5$ expresses that fact. After the signal (two lamps, in the poem) Paul Revere's knowledge of the event "coming by sea" is certain, and $P_a = 1.0$ expresses that fact. The information I received is defined quantitatively as

$$I = K \log (P_a/P_b).$$

In this definition the constant K determines in what units the information is to be expressed. If logarithms to the base two are used, and $K = 1$, the information is expressed in binary digits, and this term has been contracted to *bits*. P_b is the probability of the event before the signal and P_a the probability afterward.

For the example given,

$$I = \log_2 (1/\tfrac{1}{2}) = 1 \text{ bit}.$$

Another pair of lanterns could have transferred information about some other pair of mutually exclusive events. In brief, N bits of information require N pairs of lanterns. This procedure and definition seem at first very special and not at all useful in general. We do not often find ourselves in a situation where our message refers to pairs of mutually exclusive events; a typical message consists of words. But words can be expressed by a series of signal pairs. Basic English contains about one thousand words and can express almost any idea. Arrange the words in a list. Take the first word of the desired message and locate it in the list. The first pair of lights can express whether the chosen word is in the top or bottom half of the list, the second pair can locate the word in the top or bottom portion of the half just identified, and so on. Ten pairs of lights will isolate any word in the list. The method is clumsy, but illustrates that any message whatever can be expressed as a series of binary choices. A familiar example of this process occurs in the game "twenty questions," where an unknown thought can always be identified by enough yes-or-no answers. In actual communication the pair of lights would be replaced by an open or shut relay, a dot or dash signal, or some other easily discernible pair.

In the example considered, Paul Revere observed the two lanterns clearly and P_a became unity. If there had been a fog, Paul might have been uncertain whether he saw two lanterns or not. Then P_a would have been less than unity. If the fog had been so dense that he could see no lanterns at all, then P_a would be one-half, the same as P_b, and no information would have been transferred. If Paul had been listening for one or two strokes of the bell instead of watching for lanterns, then the sound of the waves and other random noises might have rendered the signal uncertain. Paul would have said, "There's too much noise here!" The word *noise* has been generalized by communications engineers to mean any disturbance which interferes with the clarity of the signals. Thus the presence of fog in the first example is described by saying, "The signals were barely discernible above the noise level." The *signal-to-noise ratio* is a basic parameter in communication theory.

The numerical measure of information is identical with the negative of the numerical measure of *entropy*, which has been used in statistical mechanics and thermodynamics for nearly a century. Some writers refer to information as *negentropy*. In statistical mechanics entropy was regarded as measuring the disorder of a quantity of matter. Negentropy therefore measured order, or, more exactly, the observer's information about that order. Thus when water freezes, its entropy decreases and the observer's knowledge of the arrangement of the molecules is greater—the observer has received information.

A striking example of the equality of negentropy and information was noted by Szilard in the operation of *Maxwell's demon*. Clerk-Maxwell had designed a thought experiment as follows: a closed chamber containing gas in equilibrium was divided into two parts A and B by a partition. In this partition was a door operated by a demon. When a molecule in A approached the door, the demon let it through. When a molecule in B approached, the demon shut the door. Eventually all molecules were in B. The entropy of the system had decreased because the molecules were better located than before —their disorder had decreased. This result was considered a proof that such a process was impossible, that no device could be invented which could do the work of that demon. Szilard pointed out that it was likely that the information or negentropy concerning the motion of the molecules which the demon needed to do his job was just equal to the decrease in entropy resulting from his activity.

Argument

Man builds models based on the information available to him. The signals which convey information from nature to man or from man to man are changed en route by many factors. If man wants his model to correspond to the "thing-out-there," he must separate from his information all extraneous factors. Presumably a complete separation is not possible, and models will always describe not only the thing itself but also the inseparable influences of other parts of the universe. Nevertheless, it seems desirable to separate out as many extraneous influences as possible.

Much of man's information about the universe comes to him by sight and sound. Both light and sound have wavelike aspects and therefore share many common properties. This chapter discusses briefly the quantitative concept of *information* and how information is conveyed by light and other radiation. Concepts basic to communication theory are described and illustrated by simple examples.

The *research cycle* (Figure VII-1) illustrates how information reaches the brain from the physical and social worlds, and lists a few of the factors which influence the information flow. The published model becomes part of the external universe and is then itself a source of signals which react on the model builder directly and through other men. This *feedback* of information into the model produces a self-correcting procedure for the production of models which correspond to the external world.

Chapter VIII

Biological Factors
Affecting Models

Human eye versus insect eye. Colorimetry. Trichromatic coordinates.
Spectrum locus. Imaginary colors. Trichromatic diagram. Eye versus
ear. Rod and cone vision. Ear sensitivity. Cybernetics. Feed-back.
Gestalt perception. Nerve conduction. Phase space. Line of behavior.
Field. Critical state. Stable field. Adaptive behavior. Homeostat.
Ultrastability. Model of exploratory behavior. Brain structure.
Abstraction. Universals. Choice.

The factors of interest here are not the limits in range and sensitivity of the physiological receptors; these limits are easily extended by the use of appropriate apparatus. The immediate concern is a study of the ways in which the structure and mode of operation of the human organs may influence the general world view of the model builder.

The human eye is an image-forming device; the lens of the eye forms an image of the external field of view upon the surface of the retina. As a result of this image formation, the brightness of this page as seen by the human eye is independent of distance. Under constant illumination the page looks equally bright regardless of whether it is one foot or one hundred feet from the eye. Of course the light energy picked up by the eye is much less for the distant object, but the distant object also has a much smaller retinal image. The ratio of light energy picked up to the area of the retinal image is constant for all distances. Hence the illumination of the retinal image is constant, and there is a sensation of constant brightness for the white page as it changes distance.

The eye of the bee does not form such an image. As the white page recedes from the bee, the page gets darker and darker until it disappears. Presumably the bee lives in the center of a spherical world surrounded on all sides by a foggy darkness a few yards away. In one direction there is a blinding light— the sun. It is no wonder that the flowers have develped such elaborate colors, shapes, and smells to guide the bee to them; nor is it surprising that the sun is the chief guide in the bee's navigational system. The work of Karl Von

Frisch in this field is perhaps the finest example of the use of the scientific method ever written.[*]

A comparison of the world as humans see it and as we imagine the bees see it suggests that our models must be profoundly influenced by our physiological apparatus. In searching for new models it is important for the researcher to know which aspects of his current models are accidents of his own physiology.

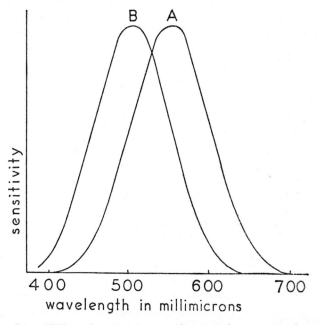

Figure VIII-1. Sensitivity curve of average human eye. *A*: daylight intensity level, cone vision. *B*: night intensity level, rod vision.

The method that has been developed for the specification of color is of great importance to the student of science for two reasons: (1) it illustrates a basic method by which a sensation can be evaluated numerically; (2) it provides an understanding of many aspects of color perception.

Light waves are those electromagnetic waves to which the human eye is sensitive. There is a fundamental relation between frequency and wave length for any kind of waves, namely

$$(\text{frequency}) \times (\text{wave length}) = (\text{velocity}).$$

Hence a particular component of a light wave can be identified by either

[*] Karl Von Frisch, *Bees: Their Vision, Chemical Senses, and Language* (Ithaca, N.Y.: Cornell University Press, 1950).

its wave length or its frequency. In specifying color it is conventional to use wave lengths expressed in millimicrons. Curve *A* on Figure VIII-1 shows the relative sensitivity of the human eye for normal level of illumination as a function of wave length. The location of the maximum at 550 millimicrons is a heritage of the evolutionary conditions of development. The distribution of intensity with wave length for sunlight shining through a few feet of sea water has its maximum in this yellowish-green region.

When white light is incident on a piece of colored glass, the distribution of transmitted intensity as a function of wave length may be measured with a spectrophotometer and plotted on a graph. Figure VIII-2 shows such a

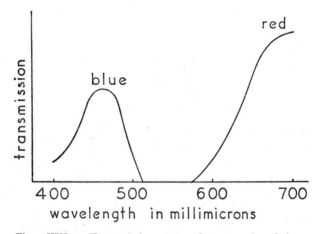

Figure VIII-2. Transmission curves of two samples of glass plate, one red and one blue.

plot for a red glass and a blue glass. The color of the glass is uniquely and quantitatively specified by such a curve. The method has two disadvantages: (1) a table of numbers is needed to specify the color; (2) when an irregularly shaped curve is given, it is not easy to visualize the color from the curve.

A second method of color specification depends on the results of experiments with a *colorimeter*. Figure VIII-3 shows schematically the construction of a colorimeter. *A* and *B* are identical white screens. *A* is illuminated as shown by three identical projection lamps, and *B* is illuminated by a lamp identical to those of *A*. Each lamp has an iris diaphragm marked 0 to 1 in such a way that 0 indicates a closed diaphragm, 1 indicates a fully open diaphragm, and an intermediate number such as 0.37 indicates that 37 per cent of the maximum light is being let through. Each lamp also has a holder such that a colored glass filter can be inserted in the beam.

The following experiment is now performed. Choose three different-colored glasses, say red, green, and blue, and put them respectively on lamps *D*, *E*, and *F*. Choose a colored glass, say orange, and put it on lamp *C*. Set diaphragm C at some arbitrary intermediate value, say 0.4, and adjust the D, E, F diaphragms. There will be found some combination of D, E, F for which screen A matches screen B as seen by a normal human observer. Negative amounts of D, E, or F may be required. A negative amount of D

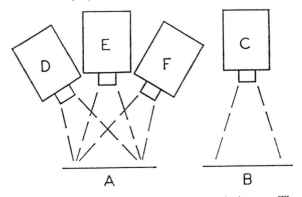

Figure VIII-3. Schematic diagram of a colorimeter. The white surface A is illuminated by a controllable mixture of three different colors of light from the projection lamps D, E, F. The white surface B is illuminated by a controllable amount of a fourth color from lamp C. The illumination of surfaces A and B may be adjusted until the two colored surfaces match as judged by an average human observer.

means that lamp D has been moved from screen A to screen B. Note that we are not trying to duplicate color C but to specify it.

We will represent the state of match by the following equation:

$$0.4C = 0.3D + 0.1E + 0.1F.$$

The numbers are the settings of the iris diaphragms. Note that the number on the left is not usually equal to the sum of the numbers on the right. However, if the setting of lamp C is doubled to 0.8, it will be found that the settings of D, E, F must also be doubled to reproduce the match. We would then have

$$0.8C = 0.6D + 0.2E + 0.2F.$$

It is found by further experimentation that the equation may be multiplied through by any constant without affecting the state of match between the fields. The relative magnitudes of the coefficients specify the color itself; multiplication through by a constant merely changes the amount of that color present. This fact permits us to specify a color uniquely by only *two* numbers. In using a colorimeter we agree to multiply the resulting equation through by whatever constant is needed to make the three coefficients on the right add up to unity. Then a color is specified by D and E only, because F

can be found by subtracting the sum of D and E from unity. Specification by two numbers is very important because two-dimensional graphs are much easier to use than three-dimensional graphs.

The experiment is now continued: the glass filters of side A are left unchanged while glasses of many colors are tried on side B. In each case it is

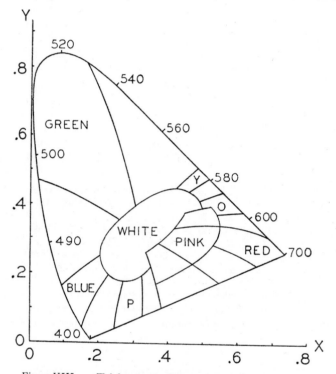

Figure VIII-4. Trichromatic diagram. The coordinates x, y of each point on this diagram specify a unique color. All colors visible to the normal human eye occur on or within the curved boundary. The locus of spectrum colors is labeled with the corresponding wave lengths in millimicrons.

found that some combination of diaphragm settings of D, E, F will produce a match, and an appropriate equation can be written.

A second experimental series is now performed: the same glass is left on side B while a series of triads of glasses of different colors is used for D, E, F. It is found that *any* three different colors on side A can be adjusted in intensity to produce a match with side B. That is, providing negative amounts are permitted, *any* three different colors may be chosen as primary standards.

In the period between 1920 and 1930, extensive experimental data were gathered using colorimeters. The different experimenters used different primary standards, but it was possible to convert from one set of primaries to another by appropriate measurements and algebraic calculation. Furthermore, it was possible to specify a color by its spectrophotometric curve (as in Figure VIII-2) and from this curve to compute the specification according

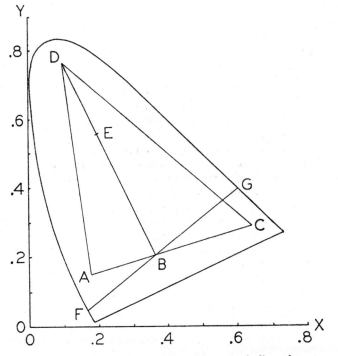

Figure VIII-5. Additive color mixing as indicated on trichromatic diagram. When the color represented by point *A* is mixed additively with the color represented by point *B*, all the resulting colors are represented by points on the line *AB*. The position of the mixture along *AB* depends on the relative amounts of *A* and *B* which are superposed.

to any chosen set of primaries. This possibility is important because a spectrophotometer can be operated automatically using a photocell in place of a human eye. The characteristics of the human eye, of course, are used in the computation.

It then remained only to reach an international agreement on what primaries to use for the three standards. An international congress in 1931 chose such a set and specified them in terms of the careful experimental measurements made during the previous decade. These three, standard, primary "colors" were chosen to be accurately computable from the measurements of a spectrophotometer and could not be used directly on a visual colorimeter. Any color is regarded as the additive superposition of X per cent of the "red" primary, Y per cent of the "green" primary, and Z per cent of the "blue" primary. Since $X + Y + Z = 1$, only X and Y are needed to specify any color. The members X, Y, Z are called *trichromatic coordinates* because a color is regarded as specified by a "point" X, Y in a two-dimensional *color space* called the *trichromatic diagram* (Figure VIII-4). A glowing solid when viewed through a spectroscope shows a continuous band of color ranging from red of wave length 700 millimicrons through violet of wave length 400 millimicrons. Each shade of color in this range corresponds to a point on the trichromatic diagram, and the whole series of colors yields a locus of points which make up the curved boundary of the diagram. The corresponding wave lengths are marked along this *spectrum locus*.

All visible colors are represented by points on or inside the spectrum locus. The spectrum locus represents colors of *maximum saturation;* the points inside the locus represent less saturated colors until the center is reached, which represents colors of zero saturation, that is, white. Black, of course, is an absence of light and is not represented on this diagram. The points outside the spectrum locus represent imaginary colors. The three international primaries which occur at the points $(X = 1, Y = 0)$, $(X = 0, Y = 1)$, $(X = 0, Y = 0)$ are all outside the spectrum locus and are imaginary. This does not matter because they are defined in terms of real colors and are used only for making computations of trichromatic coordinates from spectrophotometric data. Regions of the trichromatic diagram corresponding to well-known color names are marked on Figure VIII-4.

This trichromatic diagram describes the effects of *additive mixing* (one light on top of another) as follows. On Figure VIII-5 all mixtures of colors A and C lie on the line AC, all mixtures of A and D lie on line AD, and so on. Suppose A and C are mixed to yield B; then B and D may be mixed to produce E. Thus all mixtures of positive amounts of the three colors ACD lie on or within the triangle ACD. From an emission curve such as Figure VIII-2, one can compute the trichromatic coordinates, but the reverse computation is not unique. The difficulty is that there are an infinite number of different curves which correspond to the same three trichromatic coordinates. This situation can be visualized easily on the trichromatic diagram of Figure VIII-5, where color B can be obtained by mixing A and C, by mixing F and G, or by an infinite number of other ways. This is a characteristic of the human eye, that component stimuli are added or superposed in such a way that knowledge of the components is lost. The ear preserves most component stimuli separately. When the eye looks at two superposed colors it sees a single color, and there is no way of knowing what the original components may have been. When the ear hears a flute and a clarinet, the components are kept separate and the trained ear can distinguish the two instruments.

The trichromatic system is a method of *color specification;* it has been developed from experimental measurements on fairly extended areas of uniform color, and predicts quite accurately the results of additive mixing under similar conditions. When small areas of different colors are close together, as in a colored picture, the situation is much more complicated. E. H. Land, the inventor of Polaroid polarizing film and the automatic-developing camera, has recently renewed interest in this phenomenon by demonstrating that the eye and brain seem to be able to reconstruct colored pictures to some extent from cues having less than three primaries.

In addition to the color vision the eye has for daylight use, a more sensitive range comes into use at night when the light is dim (see Figure VIII-1). This second range is not color-sensitive. The surface of the human retina has two different types of nerve receptors intermingled, cone-shaped receptors for color vision and rod-shaped receptors for low-intensity use. This double set is a great advantage. Owls have only rods and can hardly see in daylight; hens have only cones and can hardly see at night. When the eye goes directly from sunlight to low-intensity light, there is a period of a few minutes before rod vision becomes effective. This process of *dark adaption* continues for many hours, so that the eye after being under low-level illumination for ten hours is much more sensitive than when adapted for only a few minutes. Those who need to see under low levels of illumination (night pilots, photographic workers, etc.) wear dense red filters over their eyes in daylight to preserve their "night sight."

The center of the retina (fovea centralis) is the most sensitive part of the retina for daylight vision; the side areas of the retina are most sensitive for night vision. To see best in the daytime, an observer looks directly at the object so that the image falls on the fovea. To see best at night, the observer looks at one side of the object so that the image falls on side areas of the retina. The survival value of this arrangement is clear; a flank attack by a predator is easily seen. This arrangement has a peculiar aspect. If an observer at night sees something dimly "out of the corner of his eye" and automatically turns his head for a better look, the thing disappears. It is not surprising that our savage ancestors believed in the existence of almost invisible spirits that roamed at night.

The cones in general are most sensitive to the greenish-yellow color of wave length 550 millimicrons, and thus arose the custom of using yellow paint for danger signals, life rafts, etc. However, there is considerable evidence that the very center of the fovea centralis is most sensitive in the red region. This is precisely the part of the retina used by an observer who is searching for the pin-point image of a distant life raft, and life rafts now are colored bright red.

Designers do not always remember that the eye sees differently under high- and low-level illumination. The orange and blue colors of certain auto license plates have a very satisfying contrast in daylight, but under low-level illumination when the eye is color blind, the luminosities of the two colors are almost identical and the plates appear to have no numbers at all.

The eye has been discussed at considerable length because models are built largely from visual data. The ear contributes to the process chiefly through language, and the senses of touch, taste, and smell contribute hardly at all. However, it is not safe to assume that the nonvisual senses do not influence our models merely because they do not contribute much directly. It is precisely the least obvious effects that are most insidious. The investigator must be aware of the pioneer scouts' advice: "When you hear noises in the night . . . , them's varmints! When you don't hear nothing . . . , them's Indians!" A thorough study of the effect of touch, taste, and smell on our world view is much needed.

The normal ear of the young adult is sensitive to frequencies from about 20 to 20,000 cycles per second. Figure VIII-6 shows the variation of relative

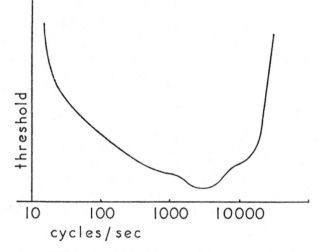

Figure VIII-6. Sensitivity of average human ear as function of frequency of sound. The curve represents the threshold of hearing, that is, the minimum sound intensity discernible at each frequency.

sensitivity versus frequency, with maximum sensitivity at about 3500 cycles per second. The absolute sensitivity is about 10^{-16} watts per square centimeter. Here, as also for the eye, evolution has produced an apparatus of ultimate sensitivity; an increase of sensitivity by a factor 10 would encounter the thermal noise level at room temperature. The frequency-resolving ability of the ear is such that about 1500 different pitches can be distinguished over the maximum auditory range. In comparison, the eye can distinguish only about 150 different wave lengths over the visual spectrum.

The human auditory process is such that one sometimes "hears" components that are not present in the stimulus. Thus a stimulus consisting of the three frequencies 400, 500, and 600 cycles per second will be heard as a fundamental of 100 cycles per second plus harmonics. If the 500-cycle tone is removed from the stimulus, the sound will be heard as a fundamental of 200 cycles per second plus harmonics. Some other characteristics of the auditory system will be discussed in Chapter IX in the section on linguistics.

Proceeding with the discussion of physiological factors affecting models, one must consider the transport of information by the nerves. The nervous system has much in common with the communication circuits studied by engineers. The field of *cybernetics* includes the study of the parallelisms between structures built by engineers and those structures in the animal body that have a similar purpose. The word *cybernetics* is derived from the Greek word for "steersman," and refers to the study of steering devices in the most general sense of the word "steering." The brain, the senses, and the nervous system constitute a physiological cybernetic device. Fire directors, autopilots, computers, telephone networks, regulators, and a host of other engineering devices constitute examples of inorganic cybernetic instruments. There are basic laws of these devices which do not depend upon whether the apparatus is made of metal or of protein molecules, and cyberneticians seek these laws.

Even before general laws are formulated, it is an advantage to realize that certain concepts are common to both organic and inorganic cybernetic devices. The concept of *feedback* is one such category. Suppose it is desired to keep the temperature of a room constant at 70°F. The temperature results from a balance between the hot air from the furnace and the cold air from outdoors. A thermometer is designed so that it turns on the hot air if the temperature is less than 70°F and turns off the hot air if the temperature is greater than 70°F. This *thermostat* is located in the room whose temperature is to be controlled. This procedure is an example of feedback. The temperature of the room may be regarded as the "output" of the heater. A signal that depends on the difference between the desired output (70°F) and the actual output (say 65°F) is fed back to the heater and controls it to produce the desired effect.

An example of feedback in a biological system occurs when a person picks up an object. The desired action is to seize the object. The eye estimates the remaining distance between the hand and the object, and signals the motor system correspondingly. In a certain type of brain damage there is a failure in the feedback system, and the hand swings back and forth past the object in a vain attempt to pick it up.

A second example of a similarity between physiology and engineering occurs in connection with the problem of Gestalt perception; that is, how does the brain classify an object as "square" regardless of its size or orientation? An engineer had designed a circuit to control the scanning of various sizes of type in an automatic reading device. A physiologist noted that the circuit resembled the fourth layer of the visual cortex of the brain. The scanning period was about the same as the "alpha rhythm" of the brain as obtained from an encephalograph. From this correspondence it was possible to build up quite a useful model of Gestalt perception.

The present state of knowledge regarding the passage of a signal along a nerve is incomplete, but one fact is well established—the response curve is a *step function.* When a very weak stimulus is applied, the nerve does not respond. As successively stronger stimuli are applied, the nerve still does not respond until a certain intensity of stimulus is reached; then the nerve transmits a signal. The magnitude of the signal cannot be increased by increasing the intensity of the stimulus. A plot of signal intensity against stimulus

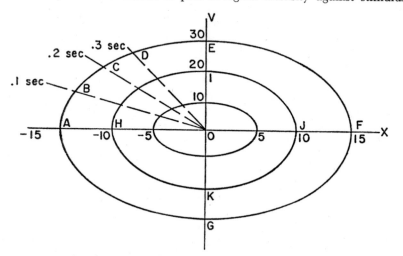

Figure VIII-7. Phase space diagram of short pendulum. The vertical and horizontal coordinates of each point on the plane represent respectively the velocity and instantaneous position of a moving pendulum bob. If the pendulum is put into the state of motion represented by point *A*, the pendulum will move so that the representative point traces out the elliptical locus *AEFGA*.

intensity has the shape of a stair-step and the minimum effective stimulus intensity is called the *threshold*. Electronic counting circuits have a similar behavior.

After each effective stimulus there is a period of a few milliseconds before the nerve has recovered and is ready for the next impulse. The nerve pulse has a velocity of about 1 to 100 meters per second depending on the diameter of the nerve; the larger nerve has the higher velocity. The pulse probably consists of some physico-chemical change in the monomolecular surface layer of the nerve. The energy for the pulse is supplied locally by the nerve and not by the stimulus.

All information about the external world must travel as a series of signals along these nerves. How does this influence our models of the external world? We do not know, but clearly here is a fertile field for cybernetics and information theory to explore. Are there kinds of knowledge that cannot be reduced to a sequence of pulses? Can the brain imagine such knowledge? The mystic who says "Yes!" should be prepared to produce a brain model to illustrate his contention. The epistemologist of tomorrow may well be a brain physiologist.

A type of brain model developed by W. Ross Ashby uses the concept of *phase space*. Consider, for example, a simple pendulum. The state of motion of

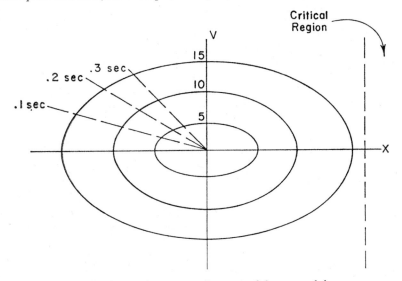

Figure VIII-8. Phase space diagram of long pendulum. Note that the velocity for a given instantaneous amplitude is less than in Figure VIII-7.

the bob is specified by two *variables*, its position and its velocity. The position of the bob is specified by its distance from the central rest point; this distance is called its *instantaneous amplitude*. Figure VIII-7 is a two-dimensional phase space in which the instantaneous amplitude is plotted as abscissa and the corresponding instantaneous velocity is plotted as ordinate. Pull the pendulum bob 15 centimeters to the left of its rest position and hold it there. It is now in state A with amplitude -15 cm and velocity 0. Release the bob. One-tenth second later it is at B with instantaneous amplitude -13 cm and instantaneous velocity $+10$ cm/sec. As time goes on, the point representing the state travels along curve $ABCD$. This curve is called *line of behavior*. At E its instantaneous amplitude is 0, but its velocity is $+30$ cm/sec. If there is no friction, the bob will continue to swing, and the representative point will continue to trace the curve $AEFGA$ until the system is disturbed. If the pendulum is started with an initial amplitude of -10 cm, then curve $HIJK$ will be traced. The phase space which contains all possible lines of behavior for this pendulum constitutes its *field*. Figure VIII-7 is drawn for a pendulum of a particular length. The length of the pendulum is a possible variable, but it is not plotted in the phase space. Such a variable is called a *parameter*. If the pendulum is lengthened, the lines of behavior change to the form shown in Figure VIII-8. Generally speaking, a fixed value of a parameter specifies a field, and a change in parameter changes the field.

Imagine now that the pendulum is located in front of an open fire. If it swings too close to the blaze, the string will catch fire and the pendulum will be destroyed. The broken line in Figure VIII-8 represents the *critical states*, and the area to the right of the broken line is the *critical region*. If the motion is such that the representative point moves along a line of behavior to a critical state, the string will catch fire. This event could be prevented by putting a wire mesh in the position of the broken line so arranged that when the bob touches the wire the length of the string is suddenly reduced to 15 cm. The bob thus is pulled away from the critical region. Speaking more generally, the occurrence of a critical state causes a change in parameter which changes the field to one where the bob cannot reach the critical region.

A field is said to be *stable* within a specified region if the lines of behavior remain in that region either by being closed curves or by leading to a stationary point. The lines of behavior of a frictionless pendulum are closed curves. The lines of behavior of a pendulum with friction are spirals which end at the origin. In either case the motion, the lines of behavior, and the field are said to be stable. In Figure VIII-8 the field is stable only in the region to the left of the critical area.

Now that the vocabulary has been illustrated, we can proceed to consider just what Ashby was trying to do and how he did it. Ashby developed this model to show that a purely mechanistic system can display *adaptive behavior*, that is, it can learn by experience to avoid dangerous situations and thus prolong its survival. A young kitten encountering for the first time the fire on the hearth displays adaptive behavior. First it approaches too close, finds it too hot, and jumps back. Then it may find a comfortably warm position and go to sleep there. If the fire blazes up it will retreat again; if the fire burns low it may move closer to a warmer spot. Body temperature is one of many *essential variables* which the kitten organism must keep within a definite region in order to survive. Other essential variables for the kitten would be its blood pressure, blood pH, breathing rate, and many others. Adaptive behavior of an organism attempts to maintain all essential variables within a region of safety and comfort.

Ashby sought to illustrate how such behavior could occur in a mechanistic system. He built a device he called a *homeostat* which displayed such behavior. His most basic contribution, however, is his formulation of the abstract properties common to adaptive systems whether they are made of metals or proteins. These abstract properties are gathered together into what may be regarded as a mathematical model of one aspect of the brain and nervous system. This model is built as follows.

An organism is represented by its list of essential variables and their survival ranges, and a system is an arbitrary choice of some of these variables. A state of a system is a set of values of the variables of the system. A line of behavior is a succession of states visualized in the phase space of the variables. The field of the system is the phase space containing all possible lines of behavior. A parameter is a variable not plotted in the phase space; when it changes, the field changes.

An organism is in a certain state. The kitten is sleeping on the hearth, the fire blazes up, and the kitten feels a stimulus in the form of a blast of heat. The point representing the temperature level of the kitten moves along a line of behavior to a critical region. At the boundary of the critical region a parameter changes automatically and the field changes. If the point in this new field remains in a stable region no further change occurs, but if the point moves into a critical region the field changes. This process continues until a stable field is encountered. A system which successively rejects fields that lead essential variables to a critical region is termed *ultrastable*. Whatever the actual structure of a living organism may be, it is apparent that the structure must constitute an ultrastable system.

Another type of model illustrating certain aspects of the brain and nervous system was built by W. Grey Walter.* This model is mechanical and illustrates the exploratory behavior of animals. It resembles a turtle on wheels and has two senses: sight (a photocell) and touch (an electric switch). It has two motors, one for movement and one for steering. The circuits and relays are so connected that, in the dark, the model moves about so that its photocell "looks around" continually. If it runs into an obstacle, it backs up a little, turns a little, and tries again. If it re-encounters the obstacle, the operation is repeated until the model has gone by the obstacle or has turned so much that it is moving away from the obstacle.

If a light is turned on, the model soon sees it and goes toward it. As the model approaches, the light becomes effectively brighter until a relay is activated which turns the model away from the light. If there are two lights present, the model wanders back and forth from one to the other. When the storage battery of the model begins to need recharging, the photocell becomes partially "blind" and the light no longer repels the model when it comes close. Under the light is a stall which the model enters and recharges its battery. After dinner it recovers its sight and wanders off for further exploration. Two such models, each carrying its own light, behave in a way strangely reminiscent of the courtship dance of certain birds.

The physical structure of the brain has been partly established, but much remains to be done. The interior part controls the automatic operations of the body. The outer layer, the cerebral cortex, controls the more sophisticated reactions of the human organism. The cortex is a few millimeters thick, has an area of several square feet, and contains about 10^{10} neurons.

* See M. Grey Walter, *The Living Brain* (New York: W. W. Norton & Company, 1953).

It is full of folds and wrinkles, and the extent of this folding seems to be associated with the level of intelligence. The control centers for different activities are localized at different parts of the cortex. The study of the brain is complicated by the fact that the regions are not sharply differentiated in function. When a local section is injured, other sections learn to carry on the functions of the missing part.

The details of brain structure are still unknown, but some broad statements may be made concerning it. The brain is made up of ordinary matter, and is subject to the physical laws, known and unknown, of ordinary matter. One aspect of the brain acts like a cross-indexed filing system of enormous capacity. The observation of a single external object is filed in an immense number of ways using the signals from the five senses. A red tennis ball would file under red, fuzzy, spherical, bouncy, and a host of other attributes; *abstraction* has occurred. The name for the arrival and filing of signals is *consciousness*. Each filing event activates some of the previous records stored under the same abstraction and under related abstractions. The name for the activation of previous records is *memory*. The "spherical" classification of the tennis ball will already contain marbles, baseballs, suns, and planets, and the related classification will contain apples, Johnny who used to play marbles with you, and so on through all the attributes of marbles and Johnny until the secondary activations are too weak to act. All of this operation is automatic; there is no control over thought. Apparent control over thought, as when one "decides" to think of something else, is an automatic response to some external or internal stimulus.

The "file drawers" of the brain are presumably definite molecular structures or field patterns in space. Each *universal*, that is, each abstractive concept, corresponds to a particular drawer. A fuzzy, unsharp concept is one which requires a cross-connection of drawers. Since these drawers have evolved and are presumably still evolving, a fuzzy concept at one time becomes a sharp concept later. A person twenty years old has replaced by sharp concepts some of the fuzzy ideas he held when younger. Similarly, the philosophers of Newton's time found his ideas strange and unsatisfactory, but a century later Kant found them to be axiomatic. A philosopher or scientist who wishes to be understood must use concepts that are sharp in his day or be content to wait until time and use sharpen the concepts he assembles.

Do these file drawers pre-exist in the new-born brain so that observation merely fills them? There seems to be no operational way to answer this question at present. If these drawers pre-exist it would seem to mean that the categories available for model building are limited to those present and their combinations. The number of combinations of even a few elements is so immensely large that this limit, if it exists at all, is not much of a handicap.

A second aspect of the brain is its ability to compute the probability of survival resulting from several possible modes of action, pick out the maximum, and direct the motor centers accordingly. This process goes on automatically and has received the ironic name of *free choice*. The brain of a student faced with the possibility of going on a date or studying for the next day will compare the probable comfort of the two actions and direct the student to one or the other according to the information available. The student describes the process by saying, "I thought about it, and decided to go on the date."

Argument

Information about the external world comes to man through his senses, and early models were subject to the limitations of the senses. In recent centuries these senses have been extended by apparatus. The human eye is sensitive to a very narrow frequency band of electromagnetic radiation, but current apparatus can measure such radiation over an immense range. The other senses have been similarly extended and calibrated. Furthermore, apparatus can be built to measure influences which are quite different from those detected by the five senses. Such biological factors no longer limit the forms of models.

However, there is a more subtle way in which man's senses can influence his models. Childhood experiences are filtered through the senses and presumably affect man's way of thinking by direct action on the growing brain. Computing machines extend the arithmetical ability of the brain, and fire-control devices extend its predictive and motor control abilities. The design of apparatus to extend other abilities of the brain awaits further investigation into the operation of the brain itself. Two models of the brain, a mathematical model and a mechanical model, are described as examples of such efforts to study aspects of brain activity.

Chapter IX

Social Factors Affecting Models

Interaction of language and thought. Wintu topological language. Language families. Hebrew grammar; root, verb, stem, sentence, divine name, shibboleth, numbers. Metalanguage. Principia Mathematica. Consistency. Decidability. Gödel's theorems. Speech perception. Pattern playback. Formants. Semantic overtones. Symbolic logic: Equivalence, truth tables, compound statements, implication, valid arguments, equivalent electric circuits.

Our models of the physical world are shaped and limited by the properties of communication channels, both of the physical and of the social world. The chief communication channel of the social world is language.

The effect of language upon the world view of a people is difficult to evaluate because it is almost impossible for the investigator to detect the conditioning effect of language forms on his own thoughts. It seems likely that language and thought interact to shape the development of each other. For example, did the Greeks excel in exact thinking because of the precision of their language, or did the precision of their language arise from the exactness of their thinking? Perhaps language and thought should be regarded as two aspects of a single, fundamental process.

Some psychologists investigating the perception of speech have encountered results which indicate that a person cannot recognize a language sound by hearing until he can produce it with his own speech apparatus. In the learning of a new and strange speech sound, there seems to be corrective feedback between the ear and the recognition part of the brain on one hand, and the speech and motor part of the brain on the other. The close connection between hearing and speaking is illustrated by the fact that children who are born deaf are usually also mute, and very special methods are needed to teach such children to speak. The interaction between the recognition of a sound and its production may be a special instance of a more general law regarding the verbalization of concepts. Teachers require that students validate their claim to recognition of a concept by expressing it in a way different from that provided by the teacher, and it is possible that this procedure is more than a testing device; the concept may not exist as a separable item within the brain storage system until it has been verbalized in different ways.

The language of the Wintu Indians of California seems to indicate a way of thinking quite different from our own. Imagine the surface of a table with a book lying on it. The remainder of the surface is bare. In English one describes the situation by saying, "The book is on the table." In Wintu one says, "The table bumps." The English phrase has already committed the speaker to an entire analytical philosophy of the situation: (1) there are two objects; (2) there is a polarity such that one object is above the other; (3) there is an implication that the book is supported by the table. None of this analysis is present in the Wintu sentence, which is purely topological. It is, of course, not certain that this language difference reflects a difference in thought process. On the other hand, it would be egotistical to expect that all humans must think precisely as we do.

The scientist who wishes to be as objective as possible in his study of the external world will try to free himself from the possible constraints of his own language. He can do this by studying other languages, especially those that differ widely from his own. The familiar foreign languages, the Romance, Germanic, Scandinavian, Celtic, Slavic, and Baltic languages together with Latin, Greek, and Sanskrit are not much use for this purpose; they are of the same language family as English, and do not display any marked differences in structure. Hebrew is of a different family and displays some interesting differences. The following languages representative of other families may be expected to show differences: Hungarian, Basque, Turkish, Chinese, Malay, Bantu, and Hopi.

It shoud be noted that a student may study languages for two very different reasons. He may wish to learn to speak and read the languages for purposes of intercommunication, or he may wish to compare the methods used to convey certain concepts. Speaking a language fluently is an art like playing the organ, and the development of accurate muscular coordination is essential for both. Comparative linguistics as a professional discipline combines the art of speaking and hearing a language with the science of identifying its concepts.

The student of science needs both kinds of language study. Because science is intrinsically international, he should read and speak Russian, French, and German in order to communicate with his colleagues. Fortunately, his colleagues in Japan, China, India, Latin America, and smaller countries usually speak English. The student of science also has a vital need for comparative linguistics, in order to acquire experience in the isolation of concepts from their language matrix. The usual language departments of a university are not much help for this type of study. They teach comparative linguistics, but only as a graduate study for professionals. There is need for a course for undergraduates (not language majors) which is designed to illustrate the expression of concepts by different language families. Pending the arrival of such courses, the student of science will have to do it himself as best he can.

The Hebrew language will be discussed here briefly as an illustration of the differences encountered. Some of the most striking differences have little or no semantic significance. The Hebrew alphabet consists almost entirely of consonants, most of which correspond fairly well to those of English and German. Hebrew is written from right to left on a horizontal line and successive lines go from top to bottom. The beginning of a book written in Hebrew is at the opposite end of a volume from a book written in English. Ancient Hebrew as written originally indicated the consonants only, but since the seventh century it has been customary to put a small sign below each consonant to indicate the sound of the subsequent vowel.

Hebrew has no present tense of the copulative verb. The English sentence, "He is a carpenter," in Hebrew becomes, "He carpenter." By contrast, Greek has two such verbs. One means, "He is a carpenter (and has been one for a long time)"; the other means, "He is a carpenter (and has just become one)." The existence of these verbs in Greek and English allows one to write, "He is," which is an incomplete sentence and does not necessarily have any meaning at all. Philosophers have attempted to give the phrase meaning, and have written long discussions of *being* and *becoming*. These concepts are so general that it is difficult to say anything definite and useful about them.

In Hebrew a general idea is expressed by a *root*, which usually consists of three consonants. The general idea is then made more specific by changing vowels, by doubling a consonant (written as a dotted single consonant), or by adding a prefix or suffix. There is no indefinite article in Hebrew, and the definite article is a prefix on the noun. Several inseparable prefixes act as prepositions. The possessive pronouns are also prefixes. Archaic Hebrew had three cases, but by Biblical times these endings had been lost. Hebrew does not use capitals. There are two genders in Hebrew, masculine and feminine, although the correspondence with sex is not marked. Concrete things tend to be masculine and abstract things feminine although these categories were not used by the Hebrews. Adjectives follow the noun they modify and agree with it in number and gender. Hebrew does not have many adjectives; nouns are modified by saying "man-of-God" instead of "godly man."

Hebrew verbs do not have tenses. There are two types of conjugations, *perfect* and *imperfect*, but these words do not refer to time. Perfect is used to indicate completed action; imperfect to indicate incompleted action. The active participle is used to express continued action in the present by writing, "The man kills," as, "The man killing."

The word *stem* has a technical meaning peculiar to the Hebrew language. Each stem has a complete conjugation and expresses a combination of voice and degree of action of the verb. Some verbs have more than twenty-one stems, but only seven are common. Hebrew has no possessive verb such as the English "have." Possession is expressed verbally by saying, "There is to me a horse," instead of, "I have a horse."

In Hebrew the main thought is expressed first and then modified to fit the specific situation. Thus, "The man said . . ." becomes, "He said, (namely) the man . . . ." The normal order of a sentence is predicate, subject, then object. A literal translation of a Hebrew sentence would be: "Declare to-you man what-good and what the Lord seek-after from-you that if-do justice and-love-of kindness and-cause-to-be-humble walk with-God-your." This same sentence in English word order becomes: "You have been shown, O mankind, what is good, and what the Lord is seeking from you. Nothing but to do justice, love of kindness, and to walk humbly with your God." *

In Hebrew custom the name of God is accorded very special respect. It is never pronounced at all and never written or printed except in reproducing the ancient texts for religious use. When reading these texts silently or aloud, the word *Hashem* (The Name) is substituted at the appropriate place. Texts which contain The Name are stored with care and reverence; when worn beyond further use, they may not be destroyed by the hand of man but are stored permanently in a fitting manner for the ministration of the hand of time. These matters are described at some length so that those who visit Hebrew literature as guests may be aware of the customs of their hosts.

Hebrew has an imperative form translated as, "Thou shalt . . . ." The negative imperative, "Thou shalt not . . . ," however, is not expressed by the imperative plus a negative, but by the imperfect plus a negative. Thus, "Thou shalt not steal," becomes, "*Lo tignov.*"

In the Hebrew alphabet the letter for *sh* differs from the letter for *s* only by the movement of a dot. The dot is of fairly recent origin; earlier written Hebrew made no distinction between *s* and *sh*. The story of the *shibboleth* (Judges XII) illustrates an occasion when the distinction was important: the man who could not pronounce *shibboleth* with the *sh* sound thereby revealed himself as an enemy and was killed.

The Hebrews (like the Greeks) used the letters of their alphabet to express numbers, the first letter for *one*, the second letter for *two*, and so on. This fact in itself is such a handicap in performing calculations that it is not surprising that neither of these peoples contributed to the numerical aspect of mathematics.

From this brief report upon the different methods used to express concepts in Hebrew, it seems likely that a study of other language families would yield material useful for the separation of concepts from language.

A concept which has proved very useful in decreasing the possibility of linguistic confusion is the notion of *metalanguage*. Object language talks about objects. For example, "This apple is red," is object language. One could substitute an actual apple for the word *apple* in the sentence and

* This translation is by Toyozo W. Nakarai. See T. W. Nakarai, *Biblical Hebrew* (New York: Bookman Associates, 1951).

express the same proposition. But, "*Apple* has five letters," is metalanguage; it is a contraction of, "The *word-for-apple* has five letters." Substitution of an apple for the word *apple* in the sentence, "*Apple* has five letters," leaves no recognizable proposition at all. One can go on and construct such sentences as, "*Apple has five letters* has four words," which is metametalanguage because the sentence is expressing a proposition about metalanguage regarded as an object of discourse. In summary, object language talks about objects, metalanguage talks about the names of objects, and metametalanguage talks about metalanguage.

In object language belief is expressed by the presence or absence of the word *not*; "Snow is white" and "Snow is not white" express opposite beliefs. In metalanguage belief is expressed by using the words *true* or *false*; "It is true that snow is white" and "It is false that snow is white" express opposite beliefs. In brief, the words *true* and *false* are metalanguage; they refer to statements about things and are never used to refer to things directly. A sentence such as "Snow is true" has no meaning.

A similar distinction exists between mathematics and metamathematics. Thus, mathematics deals with quantities (symbols) but metamathematics deals with theorems about symbols. An example of the importance of these notions is afforded by two metamathematical theorems proved in 1931 by Kurt Gödel. To understand the situation we must realize that much of the most impressive work in mathematics during the last century has concerned itself with a study of the fundamental logic of mathematics. Whitehead and Russell's *Principia Mathematica* (1910–1913) was an attempt to develop mathematics upon a logical basis using the methods of symbolic logic. *

A mathematical system consists of a set of symbols and operations and a method of proof. The operations and method of proof are independent of the meaning of the symbols. However, it is hoped that, whenever meanings are assigned, provable propositions will be intuitively true, and intuitively true propositions will be provable. Consider a particular proposition S expressed in the symbols and operations of the system. There are four possibilities:

(1) S can be proved in the system;
(2) the negation of S can be proved in the system;
(3) both (1) and (2) can be proved in the system;
(4) neither (1) nor (2) can be proved in the system.

If case (3) occurs, the system is said to be *inconsistent*. If case (4) occurs, the system is said to be *incomplete* and the statement S is *undecidable*.

It was hoped that the program started in the *Principia Mathematica* (*PM*) would produce eventually a *consistent* and *complete* system where provability would correspond to intuitive truth. In 1931 after study of the *PM* system, Gödel proved two metamathematical theorems:

* A. N. Whitehead and B. Russell, *Principia Mathematica* (New York: Cambridge University Press, 1925–1927).

(1) The *PM* system is incomplete.

(2) The consistency of the *PM* system cannot be proved within the *PM* system itself.

The proof referred explicitly to the *PM* system, but the same type of proof would appear to be applicable to any such systems. Gödel's theorems have since been proved by several other mathematicians using different methods. There seems little doubt that there is an inherent divergence between provability and intuitive truth.

Gödel proved the first theorem by constructing an undecidable proposition. He made an interesting application of metalanguage methods. By an ingenious use of the properties of prime numbers, Gödel was able to assign a unique numerical designation to each theorem of his system. Conversely, given any arbitrary number it was possible to find the corresponding theorem (if one existed) in the system. These designation numbers constituted a vocabulary of a metalanguage. Using the symbols and operations of his system, Gödel constructed the statement, "The theorem having number designation N cannot be decided." He then computed the number designation for this theorem, and substituted it for the variable N. The theorem then states its own undecidability.

The reader must not expect the description above of Gödel's theorems to be complete and precise. Verbal language is too clumsy for such purposes. For an exact statement of the situation, one must consult Gödel's papers or the extensive literature on the subject written by other mathematicians using the language of mathematics.

In recent years extensive research has been done on the production and perception of speech. This work has illuminated both the psychological and engineering aspects of language, and has also contributed to linguistic science. Some of the work of the Haskins Laboratories (New York) will be described as an example of this type of research.

The Bell Telephone Laboratory developed a device that can record the acoustic spectrum of human speech continuously as it is spoken. The Haskins Laboratory constructed a device to "play back" the recorded acoustic spectrum and thus reproduce the sounds that were originally recorded. This *pattern playback* will also synthesize into speech-like sounds idealized spectra that have been drawn by hand. This latter possibility has permitted a most interesting series of experiments that isolate and identify the basic cues the brain and nervous system use in the perception of speech.

In order to obtain the minimum pattern necessary for intelligible speech, one starts with an accurate copy of the actual spectrogram and prepares a series of drawings which omit successively more and more detail. These are played back in succession for listeners who report the minimum pattern for which intelligibility is retained. This minimum pattern and experiments suggested by it provide a powerful tool for the study of the perception of speech and allied linguistic problems.

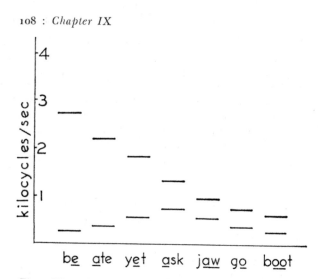

Figure IX-1. Idealized frequency spectra of seven vowel sounds.

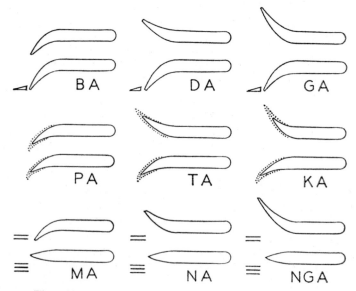

Figure IX-2. Idealized frequency spectra of the vowel *a* in combination with nine consonants.

In a highly oversimplified way, speech may be regarded as a series of steady tone carrier waves (the vowels) which are frequency modulated by the consonants. The changes from one vowel through a consonant to another vowel provide many pattern variations which complicate the study of the consonants. Figure IX-1 shows the idealized spectrum patterns of seven vowel sounds. Figure IX-2 shows how several consonants modulate the basic frequencies of the vowel "a". The frequency regions of high intensity which appear on the original spectrum and which are drawn in an idealized fashion for playback are called *formants*. Figure IX-3 shows the formants

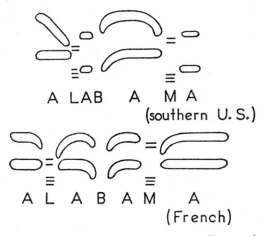

Figure IX-3. Idealized frequency spectra (formants) of word *Alabama* as pronounced in Southern United States and in French.

for the word *Alabama* as pronounced in the southern United States and as pronounced by a Frenchman. These particular formants were not idealized from the records of recorded pronunciations, but were actually synthesized by the experimenters; when played back they gave quite satisfactory renditions of the intended sounds.

The relationship between formants and phonemes is under investigation. The study of formants has provided clues to the operation of the speech centers of the brain. In general, it is observed that perceived similarities and differences between speech sounds correspond more closely to articulatory behavior in reproducing the sound than to the actual acoustic details present in the spectrogram.

One defect of verbal language has been mentioned previously; it is not as precise and concise as the language of mathematics. The lack of precision has been remedied somewhat by giving technical meanings to ordinary words. Thus *work* has a definite quantitative meaning in physics, and the word *information* has a quantitative definition in engineering. There appears to be no remedy for the essential verbosity of verbal language.

A second defect of verbal language for the purpose of the scientist is the presence of *semantic overtones*. It is almost impossible for an educated citizen of the United States to hear the word "fourscore" without thinking of the Civil War, of Lincoln, and Gettysburg. Such semantic overtones are the very essence of poetry and literary prose when the writer is trying to convey a mood. These overtones are the stock in trade of the political orator and the provocateur. For the scientist who is trying to express a fact without also evoking an emotional response, verbal language is an awkward tool. The words have all been used before, often in emotional situations, and the word recalls the emotion whether one wants it or not.

Symbolic logic is an attempt at a precise, concise, language expecially adapted for abstract reasoning. Statements are represented by letters. For example, let P represent "Roses are red" and Q represent "Violets are blue." Then $\sim P$ (read *not* P) means "Roses are not red." P & Q (read *P and Q*) means "Roses are red, and violets are blue." P & ($\sim Q$) means "Roses are red and violets are not blue." The statements represented by $P, Q, R, \ldots$ may be true or false and may have no logical connection with each other. As will be seen, the symbols described so far are sufficient for a complete symbolic logic. The system, however, would be very clumsy and bulky, so it is desirable to introduce some abbreviations for combinations of symbols which occur quite often and correspond to simple grammatical ideas. Consider the statement $\sim[(\sim P)$ & $(\sim Q)]$, which means "You cannot have not P and not Q simultaneously. This means you can have P or Q or both of them. If we introduce the symbol "$\vee$" meaning "one or the other or both," then we have *equivalent* ways of expressing the same statement, and can write

$$P \vee Q \equiv \sim[(\sim P) \text{ \& } (\sim Q)],$$

where the triple bars mean "equivalent."

The English language has no single word to express the idea of the symbol "$\vee$," but the Latin conjunction *vel* means precisely "one or the other or both." Another Latin conjunction, *aut*, means "one or the other but not both," and symbolic logic uses the symbol "$\underline{\vee}$" for the idea expressed by *aut*. English uses the same word *or* for either of these ideas, so that sentences containing the word *or* can mean two different things. In English one must use two words and say, "*Vel* means *inclusive or* while *aut* means *exclusive or*." English writers made desperate by this lack sometimes use *and/or* for *conjunctive or*.

We have said that $P, Q, R, \ldots$ may be true or false. Let us consider what cases can arise when the truth or falsity of the statements are considered. The list of possible cases is called a *truth table*.

If we limit ourselves to the usual case of a two-valued logic, then a statement must be true or false and the truth table for P and ($\sim P$) is:

P	$(\sim P)$
T	F
F	T

The idea of undecidable statements can be used within a two-valued logic (Gödel did so) because it can be considered that the statement has only two possible values (T or F) whether or not one knows which case is present. On the other hand, one can class statements as true, false, or undecidable and have a three-valued logic.

If there are two statements, then the list of possible cases has four combinations.

	P	Q
(1)	T	T
(2)	T	F
(3)	F	T
(4)	F	F

The truth table for P & Q can be constructed intuitively by considering logically each pair in succession. In row (1) it is intuitive that when both P and Q are true, then P & Q is also true. In rows (2) and (3) one of the pair is false so P & Q is also false in each case. In row (4) both of the pair are false, so P & Q is false also. These results are summarized in the truth table:

P	Q	$(P \& Q)$
T	T	T
T	F	F
F	T	F
F	F	F

By considering each row individually, one can construct the truth table for the other two symbols in a similar fashion:

P	Q	$(P \vee Q)$	$(P \veebar Q)$
T	T	T	F
T	F	T	T
F	T	T	T
F	F	F	F

From these basic truth tables one can construct the truth table of a compound expression.

The compound statement $\sim [(\sim P) \& (\sim Q)]$ turns out to have the same truth table as $P \vee Q$; statements which have the same truth tables are said to be equivalent. The statement $\sim [(\sim P) \& (\sim Q)] \& [\sim (P \& Q)]$ has the same truth table as $P \veebar Q$ and is therefore equivalent to it.

Two further symbols, $P \rightarrow Q$ and $P \leftrightarrow Q$, complete the usual list of operations. Their basic truth tables are:

P	Q	$P \rightarrow Q$	$P \leftrightarrow Q$
T	T	T	T
T	F	F	F
F	T	T	F
F	F	T	T

The statement $P \rightarrow Q$ may be read as, "P implies Q," or, "If P, then Q," or, "P is a sufficient condition for Q." The statement $P \rightarrow Q$ is equivalent to $\sim[P \,\&\, (\sim Q)]$, and the statement $P \leftrightarrow Q$ is equivalent to $(P \rightarrow Q) \,\&\, (Q \rightarrow P)$. The statement $P \leftrightarrow Q$ may be read, "P is equivalent to Q," or, "P is a necessary and sufficient condition for Q."

One valuable use of symbolic logic is to check the validity of arguments. An argument is *valid* if, for the cases when all premises are true, the conclusion is true. For example, consider the argument

1st premise	$P \rightarrow Q$
2nd premise	P
Conclusion	Q

This argument is read, "If P implies Q, and P is true, then Q is true." A verbal example of this argument is, "If Socrates is a man, then Socrates is mortal; but Socrates is a man, therefore he is mortal." Examination of the truth tables for this argument shows that the conclusion is true for all cases when both premises are true—that is, the argument is valid.

By the same method the following argument may be shown to be invalid:

1st premise	$P \rightarrow Q$
2nd premise	Q
Conclusion	P

Symbolic logic has an interesting and useful correspondence to electrical circuits. Consider the circuit shown in Figure IX-4A. Two simple open-or-shut switches are connected in series. Each switch has two positions, and we set up the correspondence that closed corresponds to *true*, and open to *false*. The possible combinations may then be listed:

P	Q	
T	T	circuit conducts
T	F	circuit does not conduct
F	T	circuit does not conduct
F	F	circuit does not conduct

We have only to make *conduction* correspond to true and *nonconduction* correspond to false in order to have this circuit correspond to the truth table for $(P \ \& \ Q)$. The symbol $\sim P$ corresponds to the situation shown in Figure IX-4B, where the switches P and $\sim P$ are mechanically connected so that when P is closed then $\sim P$ is open, and when P is open then $\sim P$ is closed.

Any symbolic logic statement may be expressed in terms of only & and $\sim$ so that the circuit elements just described may be connected to represent any statement. However, the circuit shown in Figure IX-4C represents

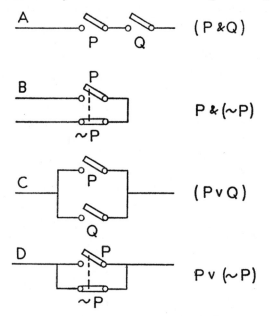

Figure IX-4. Electrical circuit elements which correspond to four compound statements. The truth or falsity of each compound statement corresponds to the state of conduction or nonconduction of the appropriate circuit element.

$(P \lor Q)$, and that in Figure IX-4D represents $P \lor (\sim P)$, and these will simplify such circuits. Since nerve fibers also have two states, conducting and nonconducting, it is tempting to suspect that the brain contains such circuits. *Logical thought* is that process of brain nerve conduction which starts from external stimuli and leads to action (say running or publishing a model) which favors the survival of the organism.

Argument

It seems likely that a man's language will have some effect on his model building, an effect very subtle and difficult to distinguish. The direct approach is to compare different languages to see how they present concepts. The differences between languages descended from a common ancestor are usually rather small; larger differences may be expected from the comparison of languages (say English and Hebrew) from different language families. A brief survey of some aspects of the Hebrew language is provided as an illustration.

Language itself is a sonic phenomenon. That the sounds of a few languages can be suggested by written symbols is a useful but not a basic feature of language. Nowadays the sounds themselves are studied to obtain clues to the irreducible features of language. A brief survey of one such study, a sonic spectrum procedure, is provided.

Ordinary verbal languages such as English are too indefinite and ambiguous for use in making the precise statements needed in science and philosophy. The semantic overtones present in all verbal languages add undesired nuances to simple statements. Symbolic logic is an artificial language which tries to avoid such ambiguities and is useful for many kinds of statements needed in science and philosophy. An elementary introduction to symbolic logic is provided to illustrate some of the concepts and procedures.

Chapter X

Concepts Used in Mathematics

Branches of mathematics. Logicalists, Intuitionalists, Formalists.
Number symbols. Course of study. Graphs of functions. Differential
calculus. Integral calculus. Theory of groups. Transformations.
Tensor analysis. Spinor analysis.

The word *mathematics* suggests to most people the study of arithmetic, algebra, geometry, and perhaps more advanced subjects dealing with space and quantity. The three fields listed have expanded laterally into neighboring areas of study, and downward into the nature of thought itself. A definition of mathematics broad enough to cover the entire region now studied is too general to convey much information. Mathematics may be defined as the study of abstract structures and their interrelations. In order to be more specific, it is convenient to divide mathematics into five general areas. The division is not exhaustive, nor are the areas mutually exclusive, but the names help to indicate the catholicity of modern mathematics: number theory, algebra, geometry, analysis, and symbolic logic. The word *analysis* here has a technical meaning and refers to those parts of mathematics which use limiting processes such as differential calculus, integral calculus, and infinite series. Specific college courses often combine the branch areas named above. Thus differential geometry studies geometry using the methods of analysis, and tensor analysis uses analysis for the study of the algebra of tensors.

The current thought processes regarding the substructures of mathematical concepts show three fairly separable tendencies. The *logicalist* tendency is illustrated by Alfred North Whitehead (1861–1947) and Bertrand Russell (1872–   ) in the *Principia Mathematica*;* the *intuitive* tendency is illustrated by the work of Leopold Kronecker (1823–1891) and L. E. J. Brouwer (1881–   ); the *formalist* tendency is illustrated by the work of David Hilbert (1862–1943). The thought processes of a particular mathematician may contain elements of all three tendencies.

The program of the *logicalist* as stated by Russell is "to prove that all pure mathematics deals exclusively with concepts definable by a small num-

---

* A. N. Whitehead and B. Russell, *Principia Mathematica* (New York: Cambridge University Press, 1925–1927).

ber of fundamental logical principles; to explain the fundamental concepts accepted in mathematics as indefinable." This program has limits, as indicated by Gödel's theorem of 1931, which showed that the internal consistency of such a system cannot be established by the method of proof available within the system. One must learn to tolerate the occurrence of undecidable statements in mathematics as well as in the world of science.

Intuitionalism regards the integers as known intuitively and basic. Kronecker remarked, "God made the integers, man made the rest." The intuitionalists have an operational point of view. In order to have "mathematical existence," a concept must be constructable in a finite number of steps. In two-valued logic, statements are either true of false; intuitionalists add a third class, "undecidable." The program of the intuitionalists is to re-examine all the theorems of mathematics. If a theorem cannot be proved using methods acceptable to the intuitionalists, the theorem is suspected of being false.

Formalism regards mathematics as a manipulation of symbols, "meaningless marks," according to definite rules. The result is a vast tautology, but a tautology of fascinating beauty and potential utility for science. Formalism uses the concept of *model*, but reverses the emphasis of the correspondence. In formalist mathematics a *model* for a set of axioms is a collection of conceptual objects which satisfy the axioms. The tendency of Chapter IV of this book is formalist although elements of the other points of view are evident.

In verbal language it is important to distinguish the concept itself from the various symbols (words) used for that concept. In the language of mathematics it is also important to distinguish the number from the particular symbol for that number. The number one hundred twenty-three may be symbolized, for example, by CXXIII or by 123. The symbol 123 is in decimal notation, that is, the system is based on ten and its powers. The symbol 123 means $(1 \times 10^2) + (2 \times 10^1) + (3 \times 10^0)$. It is possible to use some of the same digit symbols (0, 1, 2, 3, 4, . . .) in numbers expressed to bases other than ten. Table X-1 compares the expression of some sample numbers in four systems with different bases. It is not obvious from a symbol what number it represents unless the base is known. For example, the symbol 11 (read one-one) means eleven in the decimal system, three in the binary system, four in the trinary system, and thirteen in the duodecimal system. It is usually safe to assume the decimal system in the absence of warning to the contrary. Modern digital computers use the binary system, and books describing such machines may also use binary numbers.

Table X-2 shows a sequence of courses in mathematics suitable for the future scientist. The third column shows when the course is taken under present conditions, the fourth column shows a possible schedule when the secondary school curriculum has been revised to permit the study of calculus in high school. The courses listed are currently taken mainly by majors in physics, but engineering and chemistry students are discovering

Table X-1

Numbers Expressed in Various Systems

Number	Decimal (base 10)	Binary (base 2)	Trinary (base 3)	Duodecimal (base 12)
one	1	1	1	1
two	2	10	2	2
three	3	11	10	3
four	4	100	11	4
five	5	101	12	5
six	6	110	20	6
seven	7	111	21	7
eight	8	1000	22	8
nine	9	1001	100	9
ten	10	1010	101	t
eleven	11	1011	102	e
twelve	12	1100	110	10
twenty-two	22	10110	211	1t
twenty-three	23	10111	212	1e
one hundred	100	1100100	10201	84
	131	10000011	11212	te

Decimal: $4657 = 4 \times 10^3 + 6 \times 10^2 + 5 \times 10^1 + 7 \times 10^0$
Binary: $1011 = 1 \times 2^3 + 0 \times 2^2 + 1 \times 2^1 + 1 \times 2^0$
Trinary: $2212 = 2 \times 3^3 + 2 \times 3^2 + 1 \times 3^1 + 2 \times 3^0$
Duodecimal: $8974 = 8 \times 12^3 + 9 \times 12^2 + 7 \times 12^1 + 4 \times 12^0$

a need for them. Students in sociology, economics, psychology, and biology are just beginning to notice that the most sophisticated research in their fields requires the same degree of mathematical preparation. The list is quite inadequate for a major in mathematics because entire fields such as number theory and topology have been omitted, and only an introduction to the other fields is provided.

Mathematics is completely abstract, and is quite independent of figures and diagrams. However, it is very convenient, especially for beginners, to be able to visualize mathematical procedures and constructs. To each function there corresponds a curve or surface, and a visualizable drawing representing the curve can often be constructed. We will illustrate the procedure using functions of one variable.

The function $y = x^2 + 3$ may be graphed by assuming a series of values for x, say 0, 1, 2, 3, . . . , and computing the corresponding values of y, that is, 3, 4, 7, 12, ... The resulting pairs of numbers (0, 3), (1, 4), (2, 7), (3, 12), . . . are regarded as coordinates of points in the x, y coordinate system, and the points are plotted on graph paper. Through the points a smooth curve is drawn. This pencil line is a picture of the mathematical curve which corresponds to the function $y = x^2 + 3$. Such a picture (a parabola) is shown in Figure X-1.

Table X-2

Schedule of Mathematics Courses for Science Majors

Credit hours*	Name of course	Present schedule year	Proposed schedule year
	Arithmetic	1–8 (Primary)	1–6 (Primary)
6	Algebra I	1 (High School)	7
6	Plane Geometry	2	8
6	Algebra II	3	1 (High School)
3	Solid Geometry	4	2
3	Trigonometry	4	2
3	Analytic Geometry	1 (College)	3
3	Differential Calculus	1	3
3	Integral Calculus	2	4
3	Differential Equations	2	4
6	Foundations of Analysis	3	1 (College)
3	Foundations of Mathematics	3	1
3	Vector Analysis	3	1
3	Matrix Algebra	4	2
3	Tensor Analysis	4	2
3	Statistics	4	2
3	Symbolic Logic	4	2
6	Abstract Algebra	1 (Graduate School)	3
6	Complex Variables	2	3
6	Real Variables	3	4

* One credit hour equals approximately 36 hours of class and study.

At any point on a picture of a curve, a tangent may be drawn. On Figure X-1 such a tangent AB is drawn at the point $(1, 4)$ on the curve. The *slope* of the tangent is the number obtained by dividing the length BC by the length AC. The *slope* of a straight line is a number which is zero if the line is parallel the x axis, and increases as the line tips up until the slope becomes "infinite" when the line is parallel the y axis. The slope of a curve at a point is defined as the slope of the tangent at that point. Thus the curve shown in Figure X-1 has slope 0 at D, slope 2 at A, and slope 4 at E.

Differential calculus concerns itself with computing the slope of any curve or surface at any point.

Integral calculus concerns itself with computing the area between part of a curve and the x axis. In Figure X-1 the cross-hatched area equals $\frac{10}{3}$ and is represented by the symbol:

$$\int_{-1}^{0} (x^2 + 3)\, dx = \frac{10}{3}.$$

The desired function is put inside the parentheses, and the left- and right-hand limit of the area indicated as shown by the corresponding values of x.

The area $\frac{10}{3}$ is obtained by using theorems proved in integral calculus. There is a mutually inverse relationship between the process of differentiation and the process of integration. If the function $y' = 2x$ is the unique *derivative* (that is, formula for the slope) of the function $y = x^2 + 3$, then the function $y = x^2 + 3$ is one of many *integrals* of the function $y' = 2x$.

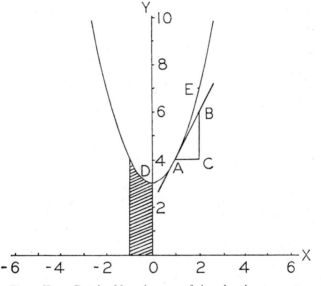

Figure X-1. Graph of function $y = x^2 + 3$ showing tangent to curve at point A, and area under portion of curve between $x = -1$ and $x = 0$. The slope of the tangent at A is the ratio of distance BC to distance AC.

It hardly seems that such simple problems could lead to the 700 pages of a typical introductory calculus textbook, but one must remember that there are lots of different curves and each type must be studied separately. The application to physics is immediate because, for example, velocity is the slope of the curve of distance plotted against time, and energy is the area under the curve of force plotted against distance. In fact, each physical quantity can appear as either a slope or an area depending on the situation at hand.

As the search for more general models is a characteristic of science, so the search for more general theorems is a characteristic of mathematics. The *theory of groups* is an impressive example of generality. The procedures of addition, multiplication, and differentiation are specific examples of the general concept of *operation* in mathematics. Operations may be performed, for example, upon numbers, symbols, and functions. The mathematician abstracts from such specific examples the general concept of *operation* which includes all examples imaginable now and, presumably, all examples which may be imagined in the future. Similarly, he abstracts the general concept of *element*, which is any conceptual entity upon which the *operation* may be performed. The physicist associates physical operations to corresponding mental operations and thus uses group theory for models of the physical world.

A *group* is a collection of elements (symbolized as A, B, C, D, etc.) and a rule of operation (symbolized by $\circ$) which has the following properties:

(1) If A and B are elements of the collection, then $A \circ B$ is an element of the collection.

(2) If A, B, and C are elements of the collection, then $(A \circ B) \circ C = A \bullet (B \circ C)$.

(3) There is a unique identity element I in the collection such that $A \circ I = I \circ A = A$ for any element A in the collection.

(4) For each element A in the collection there exists an *inverse* element A' such that $A \circ A' = I$.

Note that to element A there correspond two *operators* $[A \circ]$ and $[\circ A]$. The operation of an operator on an element $[A \circ]B$ produces $A \circ B$, another element. The operation of an operator $[A \circ]$ on another operator $[B \circ]$ produces a third operator $[A \circ B \circ]$.

One example of a group consists of the integers (including zero and negative integers) as *elements*, and *addition* as the operation. Here the identity operation I is addition of zero, and the inverse of any element is its negative.

The same set of elements using multiplication as the operation and unity as the identity element does not form a group because requirement (4) is not satisfied; the attempt to form an inverse fails because the inverse of an integer is not an integer.

A second example of a group consists of the real numbers (except zero) as elements, with multiplication as the operation and unity as the identity element.

Both examples given so far have had an infinite number of elements in the group. There are also finite groups with a specific finite number of elements. An example of such a group consists of the four elements $+1$, -1, $+i$, $-i$ with multiplication as operation and $+1$ as the identity element.

A fourth example of a group consists of the six permutations of the letters a, b, c. The six elements are the permutations abc, acb, bca, bac, cba, cab, and the operation is the process of rearranging the letters. The identity rearrangement is that of not rearranging at all. The inverse of abc is cba, and similarly for the others.

A fifth example of a group consists of the four operations of clockwise rotation by $0°$, $90°$, $180°$, $270°$ of a square in a plane coordinate system. The identity rotation is $0°$, and the inverse operations are the corresponding counterclockwise rotations. These operations leave the observable orientation of the square unchanged; the square is said to be *invariant* under this group of operations.

To each group there may be associated a corresponding group having square matrices as elements and matrix multiplication as operation. Such a group of matrices is called a *representation* of the original group. The possibility of representing any group by a group of square matrices indicates the enormous utility of matrices in both mathematics and physics.

Some groups are such that, for any two elements A and B, the combination $A \circ B$ is always the same as $B \circ A$. Such groups are described as *commutative*. A set of elements forming a commutative group to which is added a second type of operation satisfying only the first two requirements of a group is termed a *ring*. The set of all integers (positive, negative, and zero) and the operations of addition and multiplication form an example of a *ring*. If each element of a ring can be expressed as a linear combination of a few elements with complex numbers as coefficients, the ring forms an *algebra*. This definition is provided to supplement the intuitive use of the word in Chapter IV.

The fifth example of a group shows that the theory of groups includes the type of mathematics needed to model the symmetric aspect of the world. The beautiful symmetries of crystals are completely described by invariant space groups. Even more fundamentally, we shall see in Chapter XI that the symmetry of our physical space gives rise to the laws of conservation of momentum and energy.

Among the operations which may form a group are mathematical *transformations*. A transformation is a rule which connects pairs of quantities in such a way that if you know one of the quantities you can compute the other. Any function is a transformation which associates the value of the function to the value of the variable. Thus the function $y = x^2$ is a transformation because, given any number for x, you can compute y and the reverse. The *transformation of coordinates* is particularly useful in science. Two observers may measure the same series of events (say the successive positions of a rocket) but use coordinate systems with different origins and different orientations of the axes. The rule which tells observer I how to compute positions in coordinate system I from the measurements of observer II with respect to system II is a coordinate transformation. In particular, the Lorentz transformations are the rules for changing measurements from one coordinate system to a second coordinate system moving at constant velocity with respect to the first. Clearly, such a transformation is necessary at the very basis of science because otherwise two different observers cannot agree that they were measuring the same series of events.

The Lorentz transformations form a group. A law of nature must be invariant under the Lorentz group of transformations. This rather technical-sounding statement merely says that a law of nature must be independent of the coordinate systems used by different observers.

The Lorentz group has two different representations, one using $4 = 4$ matrices and one using 2×2 matrices. The $4 = 4$ matrices are operators which can act on 4-vectors. These 4-vectors are first rank *tensors*, and by multiplication one encounters higher-rank tensors and the whole subject of tensor analysis.

The 2×2 matrices have complex numbers for elements and are operators which can act on complex 2-vectors. These complex 2-vectors are first-rank *spinors*, and by multiplication one encounters higher-rank spinors and the whole subject of spinor analysis. Thus it arises that tensors and spinors are the hypernumbers which are most appropriate to express physical laws in a universe where several observers can agree on measurements and thus permit the development of science.

Argument

The traditional branches of mathematics are listed, and the three major schools of mathematical thought are described briefly. It is important to be able to separate the concept of a number from the words and symbols used to name that number. For this purpose Table X-1 displays some familiar numbers identified by their English names expressed with respect to four different bases. A list of mathematics courses suitable for science students (Table X-2) is provided as an orientation for readers whose academic experience lies in other fields. Typical mathematical concepts of great use to scientists are described and illustrated.

Chapter XI

Concepts Used in
Physical Science

Length, mass, time. Velocity, acceleration, force. Impulse, momentum.
Work, energy. Conservation laws. Field, potential. Maxwell
equations. Electromagnetic spectrum. Temperature, heat, entropy.
Laws of thermodynamics. Postulates of quantum mechanics.
Isomorphic models. Complementarity.

All measurements of the physical world can be expressed in terms of three fundamental quantities: *length*, *mass*, and *time*. The standard unit of length is the *meter*, the distance between marks on a metal bar preserved by the French Bureau of Standards, and all other meter scales are ultimately calibrated by means of the prototype meter. A direct measurement of the length of an object is made by the operational procedure of setting a calibrated scale along the object and reading off the appropriate subdivision.

The standard unit of mass is the mass of a metal cylinder preserved by the French Bureau of Standards. All other standard masses are ultimately calibrated against the prototype kilogram. A direct measurement of mass of an object is made by an operational procedure. If an analytical balance is used, the standard is regarded as *gravitational mass*; if an inertia balance is used, the standard is regarded as *inertial mass*. Both methods yield the same numerical result for the same object.

A specific object, say a person, has two different properties which must be carefully distinguished. The *mass* of a person specifies his inertia, that is, resistance to change of motion. Mass is measured in kilograms. The *weight* of a person specifies the gravitational force which acts on him and is expressed in pounds. A certain person on the surface of the earth might have a mass of 75 kilograms and a weight of 165 pounds. The same person on the surface of the moon would have the same mass, 75 kilograms, but would weigh about 30 pounds.

The standard unit of time is the *second*, which is ultimately specified by the duration of one of the recurrent motions in nature—the revolution of the earth around the sun. A certain laboratory refers its time measurements to its own standard clock. This clock is calibrated against radio time signals from the Bureau of Standards, which in turn calibrates its master clock from the revolution of the earth as measured by sighting at the fixed stars. For the scientist, time is defined operationally as "the number read from this calibrated clock."

After the three basic units—meter, kilograms, second—are defined, one proceeds to the compound quantities. The simplest of these is *velocity*. If an object travels 30 meters in 3 seconds, its average velocity is 30 meters divided by 3 seconds, that is, 10 meters/second. The unit of velocity is thus the *meter per second*, abbreviated as *m/sec*. Note that the process of division is explicitly indicated by the slanting line. All compound units can be thus referred to the basic three units, but in practice one often renames common combinations. For example, the *coulomb/second* is renamed the *ampere*.

Length, mass, and time are *scalar* quantities, that is, they are describable by hypernumbers with one element. *Displacement* on a surface is a vector quantity and requires a hypernumber with two elements, the first to specify the magnitude of the displacement and the second to specify the direction. For example, the displacement of Boston from New York is 200 miles at 55 degrees east of north. Velocity is also a vector quantity; for example, one would say, "The velocity of the car is 50 m/sec at 30 degrees east of north."

The next compound quantity is *acceleration*, also a vector quantity. Suppose a car accelerates from rest to 30 m/sec in 10 seconds; the quantitative measure of the acceleration is obtained by dividing the change in velocity by the interval of time required. The result is 3 meters/second each second, usually abbreviated to 3 m/sec². Note that the compound unit, as it were, preserves and indicates the process by which the quantity was obtained.

Now that the units of mass and acceleration are defined, we can use Newton's second law (force equals mass multiplied by acceleration) to define a unit of *force*. This new unit of force, the *kilogram meter/second²* is named the *newton*. The *pound* equals about 4.5 newtons.

The quantity *work* is defined quantitatively as the product of force applied times distance moved in the direction of the force. It is a scalar, and the unit *newton meter* is renamed the *joule*.

One can proceed in a similar fashion to build up other compound units. For example, pressure is newtons/m², density is kilograms/m³, and so on. Fortunately, only a few of the infinite number of unit quantities obtainable in this way are useful in making predictions in physics. The early history of physics concerned itself with finding which of these combinations were useful and which were not. Let us use M for mass and V for velocity. The vector quantity MV was found useful and named *momentum*. The scalar quantity $\frac{1}{2}MV^2$ was found useful and named *kinetic energy*. Products such as MV^3 and M^2V occur too seldom to be honored by special names.

Science is concerned with prediction. When a quantity does not change, prediction is particularly simple. A quantity which remains constant during a given process is said to be *conserved*. When two steel balls collide, the total momentum of the pair (the vector sum of the two separate momenta) is conserved. This is an example of the law of *conservation of linear momentum*. In this example the total energy (the scalar sum of the two separate kinetic energies) is *not* conserved, but in the low-energy collision of atoms energy *is* conserved.

Conservation laws are indications of symmetry in nature. An object may move along a line or rotate or both. The law of conservation of linear momentum holds when the motion is invariant under spatial translation of the coordinate axes of the observer. The law of conservation of energy holds when the motion is invariant under temporal translation of the coordinate axes of the observer.

The concept of *field* is one of the most basic ideas of contemporary physics. A *field* is a region of space where a test object experiences its specific force. The vector quantity *field intensity* is measured by the force which acts on a unit test object.

For the *gravitational field* the unit test object could be a small piece of metal having a mass of one kilogram. The space surrounding the earth is a gravitational field. Near the surface of the earth a kilogram mass suspended from a spring balance indicates that the field intensity is 9.8 newtons per kilogram directed toward the center of the earth. When measurements are made farther from the earth, the field intensity decreases as the inverse square of the distance from the center of the earth. In principle the field intensity never becomes zero even at enormous distances, but it does become unmeasurably small.

The space surrounding a stationary electron or a collection of stationary electrons is an example of an *electric field*. The space surrounding a magnet is an example of a *magnetic field*. Fields may be mapped by making a scale drawing of the *source* of the field (that is, the earth, electron, or magnet) and drawing curves such that the tangent at any point gives the direction of the field at that point. A mapping of the field of the earth or the electron would consist of a family of radial lines converging toward the center of the the earth or the electron. The familiar pattern of lines formed by iron filings near a magnet constitutes a mapping of the magnetic field of the magnet.

The concept of *potential* is closely associated with the concept of *field*; the two are easiest to understand in their mutual relationship. *Field intensity* is a vector quantity that describes the behavior of a unit test object within a region of space by specifying the force which acts at each point of the space. *Potential* is a scalar quantity that describes the behavior of a unit test object by specifying the *work* needed to bring the test particle to each point of the space. The test particle is brought to the point of interest from a great distance where the field force on the particle is negligible. The path followed does not affect the total work done. In the language of mathematics, one says that the particle is brought *in from infinity* and that the zero of potential is *taken at infinity*.

The upper part of Figure XI-1 shows a map of the electric field in the vicinity of a pair of charges, one positive and one negative. The solid lines are *lines of force*; the tangent to one of these curves at any point gives the direction of the force on a positive test particle at that point. The broken lines are lines of constant potential, or *isopotential* lines. The field, of course is three-dimensional, but it is axially symmetric about the line *AB* connecting the two charges. The upper part of Figure XI-1 is a map of conditions in

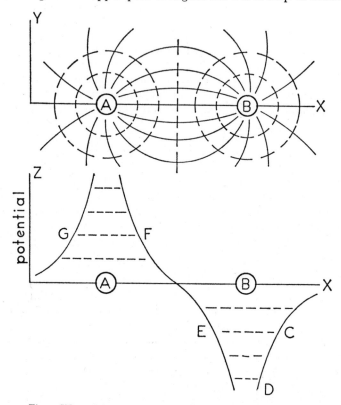

Figure XI-1. Map of electric field and potential in vicinity of positive charge *A* and nearby negative charge *B*. Upper map shows lines of force (solid lines) and isopotentials (broken lines). Lower map shows cross section of potential surface with isopotentials indicated by broken lines.

any plane through the line *AB*. The field conditions in this plane may be visualized by plotting the potential at each point of the plane on a *Z* axis perpendicular to the plane regarded as containing the *X* and *Y* axes. The locus of these plotted points make up a surface. A vertical section through this surface is shown in the lower part of Figure XI-1. There is a mountain centered at *A* and a valley centered at *B*. The broken lines are then the contour lines of the map, and the solid lines indicate the direction of the gradient of the sloping surface. A ball placed at any point on the gradient line on the mountain would tend to roll down the mountain in the direction of the gradient line.

The field intensity and potential are equivalent descriptions of the field, and each can be computed from the other. When potential is plotted against distance as in the lower part of Figure XI-1, the field intensity at any dis-

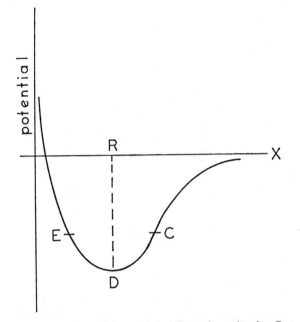

Figure XI-2. Potential curve for diatomic molecule. One atom is located at origin. The curve indicates the potential encountered by the second atom as a function of the distance *x* between the atoms. The equilibrium distance *OR* corresponds to potential minimum at *D*.

tance is just the negative of the slope of the curve at that distance. For example, on the lower part of Figure XI-1, for large (infinite) distances the slope is zero; the field intensity at infinity is zero. At *C* the slope is positive and the force is negative, indicating a force toward the left, toward *B*. At *D* the slope is approaching infinity because of the close approach to the charge: the inverse square law model of force from a charge is not valid for very small separations. At *E* and *F* the slope is negative and the force is positive, toward the right, where charge *B* is located. At *G* the slope is positive and the force is negative, toward the left, away from charge *A*.

Figure XI-2 is the potential curve for the two atoms of a diatomic molecule, say the hydrogen molecule. One of the atoms is at the origin. The curve shows the shape of the changing potential as a function of distance from the atom at the origin. For large distances the slope is zero and the force is zero. At *C* the force is toward the left, at *E* it is toward the right, and at *D* it is zero. This tells us that the second atom would normally be at the distance *R* from the first atom, and if disturbed would oscillate about this "rest" position. The second atom, of course, just moves back and forth on the horizontal axis, but one can visualize the oscillation by imagining

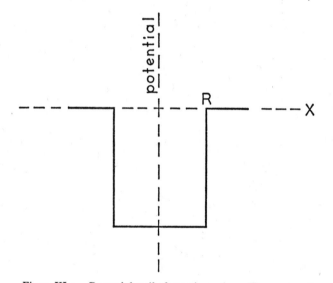

Figure XI-3. Potential well of atomic nucleus. The center of the nucleus is at the origin. The "square well" is an idealized potential which permits fairly easy calculation of some properties of the nucleus of an atom.

a ball rolling back and forth through the valley between *C* and *E*. If the ball obtained energy from outside the system, it might roll off toward the right and not return. This corresponds to the fact that, if the hydrogen molecule is given enough energy, the two atoms will separate—a process called *dissociation*.

Potential curves illustrate the redundancy of the concept of "force" because one can "explain" the stability (staying together) of the hydrogen molecule just as well by saying, "The potential curve has a minimum," as by saying, "The force of atom *A* on atom *B* tends to cause *B* to stay at distance *R* from atom *A*."

The potential curve method is especially useful for describing the nucleus where the forces acting are extremely complicated and not yet subject to exact description. Figure XI-3 shows a highly oversimplified potential curve, the so-called *potential well* of the nucleus. The center of the nucleus is at the origin. The curve tells us that the force on a nuclear particle, say a neutron, is zero inside the radial distance R, zero outside that distance, and infinite (very large) at R. If we visualize the situation as a cross section of an actual dry well, a nuclear particle is like a mouse that can move freely around the bottom of the well or around the flat ground surrounding the well, but cannot get from the bottom of the well to the surface of the ground unless someone outside provides him with sufficient energy. On the other hand, no energy is needed for either the mouse or the particle to "fall into" the well.

Having considered the electric and gravitational field, we must proceed to the magnetic field. The lines of force of a magnetic field can be traced using a small magnetic compass; the north pole of the compass acts as the test object for the field. There is an intimate relation between electric and magnetic fields. The empirical facts were discovered during the nineteenth century by a large number of experimentalists, and put into mathematical form by James Clerk-Maxwell (1831–1879). The experimental facts are essentially that (1) a moving electric charge (say an electron) produces a magnetic field and (2) a moving electric charge crossing an already existing magnetic field finds itself pushed sideways. There are four Maxwell differential equations when written in vector form. The first specifies how electric fields arise from electric charges, the second describes how magnetic fields are related to the fact that magnetic poles always occur in pairs—one north and one south pole. The third equation specifies that a changing electric field gives rise to a magnetic field, and the fourth describes how a changing magnetic field gives rise to an electric field. The four Maxwell equations constitute a three-dimensional model of electromagnetic phenomena. There is also a four-dimensional relativistic model in which there are two tensor equations, and the electric and magnetic fields are regarded as two aspects of one basic entity. The two models, of course, are equivalent.

The Maxwell equations describe that aspect of nature which gives rise to the phenomenon we call *light*. If a changing electric field is generated by causing electrons to surge back and forth along a wire, then a changing magnetic field also arises and the two change rhythmically together in the same region of space. At low frequencies, say a few hundred cycles per second, the changing electromagnetic field exists only near the wire. However, when the frequency rises to a few million cycles per second or higher, the pulsing electromagnetic field propagates itself away from the wire at a velocity of 300 million meters per second. Thus arises the electromagnetic wave. In such a wave the changing electric field produces a changing magnetic field, and the changing magnetic field produces another changing electric field in a lightning-fast game of leapfrog. Light is an electromagnetic wave having a frequency between 430 and 750 million million cycles per second; the human eye is sensitive to frequencies in this range, and the retinal impulses to the brain is called the sensation of light. The various frequency ranges of electromagnetic radiation have been given different names as they were discovered and investigated historically. The whole range of frequencies is called the *electromagnetic spectrum*. Table XI-1 lists

Table XI-1

Electromagnetic Spectrum

Name	Typical frequency*	Typical receiver
Gamma rays	10^{20}	Scintillation counter
X-rays	10^{18}	Ionization chamber
Ultraviolet rays	10^{16}	Photographic film
Visible light	10^{14}	Eye
Infrared rays	10^{12}	Bolometer
Radar waves	10^{10}	Radar apparatus
Television waves	10^{8}	T.V. set
Radio waves	10^{6}	Radio set

* 10^{20} means 1 followed by 20 zeros.

the names of various regions, a typical frequency for each, and a typical device which is sensitive to such frequencies.

The concept of energy, which has proved basic in mechanics and in the physics of fields, is also fundamental for thermodynamics. The development of the steam engine near the beginning of the nineteenth century led to a surge of interest in the computation of the mechanical energy (work) available from a given amount of thermal energy (heat). The basic experimental facts are that objects can be classified qualitatively as hot or cold by touching them, and that when a hot object is in contact with a cold object, the two soon reach an equilibrium condition where both feel the same. The invention of the thermometer permitted a quantitative measurement of the property described qualitatively by the adjectives *hot* and *cold*.

An early model of these phenomena postulated the existence of a substance named *caloric*; the temperature of a substance depended directly on its caloric content. When a hot object was in contact with a cold object, caloric flowed from the hot object to the cold object until their temperatures were the same. The notion that caloric was a substance was revised when it was found that (1) caloric appeared to have zero mass because there was no measurable change in the mass of an object when it was heated and (2) caloric was not conserved, that is, caloric could be created in a body in unlimited amounts by doing frictional work on the body. The conclusion that caloric was not a substance was valid [because of reason (2)] even though reason (1) is now known to be invalid; a body does increase in mass when it is heated, but the increase is unmeasurably small.

The revised model postulated that the temperature of a body was a measure of the average kinetic energy of the chaotic motion of the particles of the body. For example, the molecules of a block of ice are arranged in a regular pattern in space. When the ice is as cold as possible (absolute zero temperature, $-460°F$), the molecules are essentially motionless at their lattice positions. If the ice is heated, the molecules begin to vibrate chaotically about their lattice positions; the molecules now have an average kinetic energy of chaotic motion, and this average, multiplied by an appropriate constant, is the absolute temperature of the ice. If the heating process is continued, the motion becomes more and more violent until the lattice forces can no longer hold the molecules near the lattice positions and the arrangement of molecules becomes disordered; the ice has melted and changed from the solid to the liquid phase. This melting occurs when the temperature has reached $+32°F$. If the heating is continued, the chaotic motion of the disordered molecules increases, but the molecules are still held fairly close together. At $+212°F$ the chaotic motion is so violent that the intermolecular forces can no longer hold the molecules fairly close together, and the molecules start flying apart; the water boils and changes from the liquid to the gaseous phase. Further heating increases the temperature of the gas; eventually the molecules are dissociated, then the atoms, and finally at a temperature of millions of degrees the nuclei themselves are knocked apart.

The intuitive meaning of the word *heat*, used as a verb, is clear enough; its meaning as a noun is very subtle, and is best left to the experts. The difficulty lies in the intuitive notion that if you put 3 joules of heat into a body, then that body ought to contain 3 more joules of heat than it did before. It is true that, if no external work has been done, the body now contains 3 more joules of *energy* than it did before, but that energy is not necessarily in the form of heat—some of it may be in the form of internal potential energy. For example, you can supply 335,000 joules of heat to a kilogram of ice at $+32°F$ and the temperature does not increase at all; the heat has been converted to internal potential energy. The difficulty with heat as a noun is that it is not conserved. For the record, then, heat is that form of energy in transit which flows from one body to another because of a difference in temperature. The word is not properly used except when the energy is flowing; there is no uniquely definable quantity which can be called the "heat content" of a body. Heat can flow by conduction, as along a metal rod; by convection, as in the air currents above a hot object; or by radiation, as in an electromagnetic wave.

We must now contrast the two concepts *heat* and *temperature*. Temperature is measured in degrees with a thermometer. Heat is measured in joules (or calories) with a calorimeter. The temperature of an object is an intensive property; it does not depend on how much of the object there is. Heat is an extensive property; it takes twice as much heat to change the temperature of two gallons of water by one degree as it does to change one gallon of water by the same amount. Temperature is a measure of the average kinetic energy of chaotic motion of the particles of a body. Heat is a measure of flow of energy due to difference in temperature.

In order to understand the laws of thermodynamics, we must define the concept of *entropy*. Entropy is a quantity which measures the disorder of the particles of a body; it is an extensive property. In contradiction to "heat content," which is not unique, the "entropy content" of a body is a unique number. Entropy depends on the temperature of a body, and increases as the temperature increases. Entropy is measured in the unit *calorie/kilogram degree*. It may be measured experimentally by long series of measurements with a calorimeter, or, if enough is known about the structure of a substance, it may be computed. It is postulated that a pure crystalline substance at absolute zero has entropy zero, and this postulate has been called the *third law of thermodynamics*. Most practical problems are concerned with change in entropy; such changes do not depend on any particular choice for zero of the entropy scale.

There are two general laws in thermodynamics:

(1) Within a thermodynamic system (say a steam engine) the heat supplied equals the work done plus the change in internal energy.
(2) The maximum work which can be obtained from a cyclic thermodynamic process equals the change in temperature multiplied by the change in entropy.

The first law is seen to be a statement of conservation of energy regarding work and heat as forms of energy.

The second law tells us that no work can be done without both a change in temperature and a change in entropy of the "working fluid" of the engine. There are many other equivalent statements of the second law.

The two laws just quoted are the historic expressions of the basic laws of thermodynamics. The same general information can be expressed in a different way which shows more clearly the tendency of thermodynamic processes. These may be called the "A" and "B" laws of thermodynamics:

(A) Work may be changed to heat at 100 per cent efficiency.
(B) Heat may be converted to work, but at efficiencies that are always less than 100 per cent and usually less than 50 per cent.

If these laws apply uniformly throughout the universe, a progressive change of work into heat without a balancing change of heat into work is indicated. Apparently the universe is "running down," and in the remote future it will consist of a disordered cold soup of matter dispersed throughout space at a uniform temperature of a few degrees above absolute zero. Another way of expressing the same prediction is, "The entropy of the universe tends always to increase." During the growth of living organisms, entropy decreases within the organism. All indications are that the surrounding environment increases in entropy more than enough to balance the local decrease. Perhaps in some remote part of time or space there is a fountain of negentropy that some Ponce de Leon of the future may seek or even find.

We have now defined a scientific and mathematical vocabulary sufficient for a brief discussion of *quantum mechanics*, the most sophisticated model yet developed of physical phenomena. Quantum mechanics includes the successful parts of many previous models: Planck's quantization of radiant energy, Bohr's quantization of angular momentum and energy states, Schrödinger's wave mechanics, Heisenberg's matrix mechanics, Dirac's treatment of electron spin, and contributions from many other physicists, chemists, and mathematicians. Quantum mechanics is assumed to apply to all physical measurements, and it includes Newtonian mechanics as a special case. It also includes the restricted theory of relativity, but its relationship to general relativity is not yet clear. In quantum mechanics the the laws of nature appear as restrictions upon the value of the commutator rather than as the solutions of differential equations as in previous models.

The following statement of the postulates of quantum mechanics is reworded from a formulation by Henry Margenau.*

(1) To every observable quantity there corresponds an operator.
(2) A measurement of an observable quantity can yield only certain specific numbers, the eigenvalues of its operator.
(3) To every state of a system there corresponds a state-function.
(4) The average of a series of measurements of an observable quantity from a system in a specific state may be computed from an expression in which the corresponding operator acts upon the corresponding state-function.
(5) The rate of change of a state-function with time may be computed from the action of the energy operator upon that state-function.

The second postulate seems very restrictive. For example, when measuring the linear momentum of a free particle, one would expect to encounter any number whatever—positive, negative, or zero. This expectation is compatible with the second postulate because the operator for linear momentum of a free particle has an infinite set of eigenvalues, namely, all real numbers, positive, negative, or zero. On the other hand, the operator corresponding to the angular momentum of the electron in the hydrogen atom has for eigenvalues only certain specific numbers—those which were listed *ad hoc* in the postulates for the Bohr model of the hydrogen atom.

From these five postulates can be derived the Schrödinger equation, which constitutes the Schrödinger model of the atom. The Schrödinger model predicts with great accuracy the measurable effects which depend on the behavior of the electrons surrounding the atomic nucleus. Quantum mechanics is currently being used to correlate and predict measurements which depend on the behavior of particles within the nucleus. The predictions are accurate enough so that theorists expect that the quantum-mechanical model will probably be valid for the nuclear domain. It is not

* See H. Margenau, *The Nature of Physical Reality* (New York: McGraw-Hill Book Company, Inc., 1950).

yet clear what additions or modifications will be needed to permit highly accurate predictions.

When it was found in 1901 that light (ordinarily considered a wave) also had particle-like characteristics, and when, in 1927, the electron (ordinarily considered a particle) was also found to have wave-like characteristics, these facts seemed parodoxical. This reaction was naïve because one must not expect the "common sense" of the macroscopic world to persist in the microworld. It is misleading to refer to the "dualistic" nature of light merely because an entity has different aspects depending on the mode of observation. The shadow of a cylinder can be observed as a disk or an oblong, but the cylinder remains a single entity. However one chooses to describe the complementary aspects of fundamental particles, this complementarity is built into the very basis of the quantum-mechanical model. For example, the mathematical expression for the state-function of a beam of photons may be reduced by one path of thought to a recognizable description of a wave, or it may be reduced by another path to a description of a particle. These two *isomorphic* models are inherent in the original state-function, which is not itself committed to either aspect alone.

The Heisenberg indeterminacy principle states that momentum and position cannot be simultaneously measured with arbitrary accuracy. Momentum and position are said to make up a "complementary pair" of quantities. Another such pair is time and energy. In 1928 Niels Bohr formulated the *principle of complementarity*, which states that there exist pairs of quantities in nature so related that an experiment designed to measure one of the quantities will interfere with the system in such a way that the conjugate quantity cannot be measured accurately. The quantitative aspects of this principle are expressed in the *principle of indeterminacy*. Later Bohr extended complementarity in a qualitative way to include philosophical questions, and suggested that free will and determinism in human behavior might be conjugate points of view such that a commitment to one of the pair would automatically eliminate the other from consideration.

Argument

All measurements of the physical world can be expressed in terms of length, mass, and time; each of these is measured by specified operations using an arbitrarily chosen standard, and the result is a single number, a scalar quantity. Compound quantities such as density, velocity, acceleration, etc., are ultimately defined and measured by measurements of length, mass, and time, and it is found that the results may be described by hypernumbers of various sorts.

Any compound quantity whatever may be defined, but only those quantities most useful for prediction have been retained for general use. Compound quantities which remain constant with time are especially useful because they simplify prediction. Such quantities are said to be *conserved*, and are described by *conservation laws*; examples are energy, linear momentum, angular momentum. Conservation laws are indications of symmetry in nature; a quantity is conserved when it is invariant under translation or rotation of axes or other aspects of axis systems which are subject to arbitrary choice by the observer.

A *field* is a portion of space where a test object experiences its specific force. *Field intensity* is a vector quantity defined at each point of the field. Three common examples of fields are the gravitational, the electric, and the magnetic field. The motion of a body in a field may be predicted from the laws of mechanics when the field intensity at each point and the initial conditions are known. The *potential* is a scalar quantity defined at each point of a field. The field intensity at each point may be computed from the values of the potential near the point and conversely.

Heat is a form of energy. If no energy enters or leaves a region, then the total energy of that region will remain constant (be conserved), but heat, being only one form of energy, may not be conserved. Thermodynamics deals with the natural laws which describe the changes of form of energy within a particular region. Thermodynamics uses only macrosopic quantities (temperature, pressure, volume, and the like), and its relations are usually independent of molecular, atomic, and nuclear structure.

Quantum mechanics is the most general model of physical behavior yet formulated. It includes Newtonian mechanics and restricted relativity, but its relation to general relativity is not yet clear. Quantum mechanics predicts very accurately the behavior of all objects outside the atomic nucleus. It is currently being applied with considerable success in predicting the behavior of objects inside the nucleus, but the task is not complete.

Chapter XII

Models in Biology

Classification. Mendel. Genes and chromosomes. Mutations. Darwin: Organic evolution. Differential reproduction. Freud: Id, Ego, Superego. Bacon: Idols.

The first general models in biology were the systems of classification invented by the plant and animal morphologists. A classification constitutes a model because it permits prediction. A biologist who classifies a new specimen by external observation is implicitly predicting that the internal organization of the specimen will resemble other members of the same class. If the prediction is shown to be incorrect by later examination, the model will be modified; that is, the classification will be changed, and, if necessary, the classification system itself will be modified to include the new data. Such classification led to a study of the resemblance between parents and progeny, and thus to the study of genetics.

The first quantitative experiments in genetics were conducted by Gregor Mendel (1822–1884) on a variety of plants. In his work on garden peas he distinguished seven pairs of contrasting characteristics: tall, dwarf; smooth seeds, wrinkled seeds; and so on. Mendel's model of the genetic process in pea plants can be formulated as a series of postulates.

(1) To each of the 14 distinguishable characteristics there corresponds a genetic factor.

(2) Each plant contains the genetic factors in pairs.

(3) A germ cell contains only one of each pair of genetic factors.

(4) The union of a germ cell from the female with a germ cell from the male produces a cell with the usual two genetic factors.

(5) The genetic factors may be divided into two classes: dominant and recessive.

(6) The presence of a dominant factor in the plant produces the corresponding characteristic. If no dominant factor is present, the characteristic corresponding to the recessive factor appears.

Let D represent the dominant factor (say tallness) and d represent the recessive factor (dwarfness). A crossing of a pure dominant strain (DD) with a pure recessive strain (dd) will produce (Dd) and (dD) in the first generation;

all plants of the first generation are tall. Crossing of the (Dd) and (dD) plants produces (DD), (Dd), (dD), (dd); in this generation there are three times as many tall plants as dwarf plants.

Mendel's work was published in 1866, but its value was not recognized until 1900 when similar conclusions were reached independently by others. By this time microscopical study of cells was well advanced, and threadlike structures called *chromosomes* were found in pairs in the nucleus of each cell. It was then possible to modify Mendel's *postulational model* to a *material model*.

The following statements about the material model are all postulates which have been inferred from extensive and cleverly planned experiments by many different investigators. The field of genetics is especially impressive because of the ingenious experiments and careful inferences of its workers.

The genetic factors, now called *genes*, are arranged in a linear array along the length of the chromosome. Each chromosome is a long, thin molecule of deoxyribonucleic acid (DNA), and each gene is a segment of this molecule. There are several hundred genes in each chromosome. The number of pairs of chromosomes is characteristic of the species; human cells have 23 pairs, mosquito cells have 3 pairs, corn plant cells have 10 pairs, and so on. Each gene is associated with a characteristic of the organism, but the genes do not act independently of each other. The nucleus of each cell of an organism thus contains a complete "blueprint" for the entire organism. The information content of such a chromosome may be as high as 10^{12} bits and is presumably stored by the identity and arrangement of the twenty some amino acid constituents which make up the deoxyribonucleic acid protein molecule.

In the normal growth process each cell divides, and the two resulting cells are exact duplicates of the original cell. Each gene has the property of being able to construct an exact duplicate of itself from the surrounding chemical raw material. If, as occasionally happens, the copy is not exact, the inexact copy is called a *mutated* gene. The mutated gene will then form exact copies of itself and the resulting organism will display the features characteristic of the mutated gene. Since it is very unlikely that more than one gene (out of several hundred) will mutate at the same time, the change in external characteristics will be small. The progeny of the mutated organism will inherit the changed characteristic.

When an organism is fairly well adapted to its environment, almost all the accidental mutations will be neutral or unfavorable. However, when a mutation occurs such that the organism is better adapted to its environment than the usual form, the new form is more likely to survive and have viable progeny. Hence, in a few generations the new form will supplant the old form. This description of the occurrence is, of course, backward; the operational way of knowing that a form is "better adapted" is to observe that it does, in fact, survive and supplant its predecessor. It is this operation of *selection by environment* through *differential reproduction* that superposes on random mutations the directionality required by an evolutionary model.

The most general model yet developed in biology is the theory of organic evolution. The basic concept of evolution may be stated concisely: (1) variations occur; (2) selection occurs. At this level of generality the model is axiomatic; the model becomes controversial only when one specifies how the changes occur and how the selection operates. In the original form of the model, Lamarck (1744–1829) postulated that the variations occurred because of effort by the individual animal and that these acquired characteristics were inherited.

As an example, the preferred food of the giraffe is tree leaves. The herd eats off the leaves within reach of the ground, and each animal is constantly stretching upward toward the higher leaves. This continual stretching upward during its life increases by a little the length of the neck and front legs. This increase in length is an "acquired characteristic" and was assumed to be inherited by the next generation of giraffes.

Charles Darwin (1809–1882) modified this model by stressing the operation of *natural selection*. Continuing with the example above, those giraffes born with longer necks and legs are better fitted to their environment (food located in tall trees) than those born with shorter necks and legs. The taller animals get more food and are more likely to survive and have progeny than the shorter animals. As long as additional height is an advantage, giraffes will continue to grow taller through the *survival of the fittest*.

The postulate that acquired characteristics were inherited soon came under criticism because no definite examples of its occurrence were observed. Meanwhile, knowledge of the mechanism of genetics was greatly increased by experimental work, and the model of evolution was modified to include this new knowledge. As always, the new model included the successful parts of the old model. The modification consisted of a new postulate regarding the occurrence of variations and a more definite postulate regarding the process of natural selection.

The new model postulates that changes occur by *mutation*, and that natural selection occurs through differential reproduction. In order to contrast the modified model with the original model, we will again discuss the situation of the giraffe although specific genetic data on this animal are not available.

We start with a population of giraffes with moderately long necks and front legs and a liking for leaves that grow in trees. An individual giraffe may succeed in stretching his neck a decicubit during his life, but this acquired increment is not inherited by his progeny. A giraffe presumably has several thousand genes which control his shape. The mating process produces new combinations of genes and gives rise to variations which are inherited. Mutations also produce variations, and these are inherited; most of these variations are neutral or unfavorable. However, if one of these variations increases the length of the neck by a half-inch, and this half-inch is an advantage to the animal, then the probability of viable progeny from this variation is increased. In a few generations the extra length becomes standard equipment for the species. The process can then be repreated until the extra length becomes a disadvantage. The variations are random, but natural selection produces a form better adapted to the environment.

We will turn now to a special area of biology, the field of psychology. Sigmund Freud (1856–1939) developed his first model in this field about 1906. Further experience with the model indicated minor modifications which were incorporated into its final form as published in *An Outline of Psychoanalysis* in 1949.*

The postulates of the model were based on inferences drawn by Freud from his observations of normal people and neurotic patients, and the predictions which he made were implicit in his method of treatment of neuroses. Freud's model was eventually a *material model*, as may be seen from his basic postulate: "We assume that mental life is the function of an apparatus to which we ascribe the characteristics of being extended in space and of being made up of several portions." The "apparatus" is the brain and nervous system which is divided functionally, and, to some extent, spatially, into three parts: the *id*, the *ego*, and the *superego*.

The *id* is present at birth; its structure and activity are the result of the previous history of the species. The id represents the influence of the past which acts directly in the individual organism through the inheritance of structure and function. It is the oldest part of the brain, the part which evolved first. Insofar as it is localized, it is the interior of the brain and its associated nerve system. It controls and directs all the automatic machinery of the body, the activity which is unconscious. The id is the source of those unlearned (by that individual) patterns of behavior called *instincts*. It responds to stimuli in a stereotyped fashion as one would expect in a blindly automatic process. Except for the activating stimuli, the id acts without influence from current external conditions or anything "learned" during the life of that individual organism. The actions of the id are actions which favored the survival of the organism in its species history, but which do not necessarily favor survival now under current conditions. The id was the entire "brain" of the organism at the stage of its evolutionary development when species survival involved only food, conquest, and procreation. Freud subsumed all of these items under one word: *eros*.

The *ego* represents a later evolutionary development than the id, and is localized in the cortex. The ego is sensitive to, and acts upon, stimuli from present conditions and from the organism's memory of its own specific experiences since it was born. It is properly called the *ego* because it is the locus of the record of present and past experiences of the *individual* organism. The evolution of the ego provides a much more sophisticated mechanism of survival than the blind instinctive procedure of the id which often led to the death of the individual organism. The ego appeared in rudimentary form in some mutation in the remote past which provided that organism *A* would not automatically attack and try to eat organism *B* upon encounter, but

* Sigmund Freud, *An Outline of Psychoanalysis* (New York: W. W. Norton & Co., 1949).

might take flight if a memory of a previous narrow escape vetoed the attack signal. The ego (and superego) is the locus of those automatic procedures which are described by the words "making a choice."

The *superego* is a development and extension of the ego, and is therefore also located in the cortex. The superego is sensitive to, and acts upon, present stimuli as related to memory of past stimuli originating in the social system. The effects of parents, teachers, and admired figures and the sanctions and taboos of the social system are channeled through the superego. The superego, in particular, includes the mechanism for learning from vicarious experience through symbols. A child (or a seeing-eye dog) learns to obey traffic lights or, at a more sophisticated level, to respond to spoken orders. The supreme achievement of the superego occurs when (for example) a man reads the instructions for synthesizing an organic compound and is able to do it although he personally has never previously encountered that specific situation.

The brain of a moth is made up essentially of the id portion alone, and the behavior of a moth is an example of the kind of activity associated with stimulus and response of the id alone. The brain of a dog contains both id and ego, but little superego; the dog's behavior therefore illustrates approximately the combined action of id and ego. Only man combines id, ego, and superego, for man is the only animal with a highly developed system for trying to transfer by education the experience of the race to each individual.

Freud tended to *personify* the three aspects of the brain and nervous system. The id hardly qualifies for personality except as a figure of speech. On the other hand, the ego and superego do not need to be "personified"; they *are* persons, or, to be more exact, they are the two components of the human person.

Freud's model is an attempt to add detail to the part of the research cycle (Figure VII-1) which describes the action of the brain. Figure XII-1 is a functional diagram of Freud's model and may be superimposed on Figure VII-1.

Freud was interested in treating neurotic patients and used his model as a guide and predictor in planning his procedures. The extent of validation of this model depends upon Freud's success in treating patients. It would seem that there is no doubt that some degree of validation has been achieved. The extent of the validation can be estimated only through an intimate knowledge of Freud's patients subsequent to their treatment.

There is a remarkable resemblance between Freud's twentieth-century model and a model described by Francis Bacon (1561–1626) in his *Novum Organum*. Bacon was recommending a "new instrument" for the advancement of scientific knowledge. The instrument was *induction*, as opposed to the *deduction* which was then regarded as essential. Bacon distinguished four influences which (in our language) distorted the shape of models. He named these distorters the *idols of the tribe*, the *idols of the cave*, the *idols of the market place*, and the *idols of the theater*.

The *idols of the tribe* have their source in human nature itself which "distorts the nature of things by mingling its own nature with it." The *idols of the cave* have their source in the individual man. Each individual "has a cave or den of his own," his own experience, which may arise from personal encounter or through vicarious experience such as reading. The *idols of the market place* have their source in the association of men with each other. The limiting

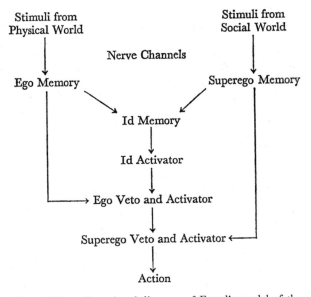

Figure XII-1. Functional diagram of Freud's model of the brain and nervous system. This figure may be superimposed upon Figure VII-1.

and distorting effect of language upon thought is one of the great *idols of the market place*. The *idols of the theater* have their source in the philosophic systems of the past, present, and future. These systems are like "stage plays, representing worlds of their own creation after an unreal and scenic fashion." In modern language, Bacon is here warning us not to confuse models with reality. It is the ever-present danger of this confusion which forces modern writers to such monotonous use of the word *model*.

Other examples of models in the general field of biology, Ashby's model of the brain and Walter's model of exploratory behavior, were described in Chapter VIII.

Argument

The first general models in biology were the systems of classification; these are models because they permit prediction. The historical development of models in genetics displays a feature common to the development of models in many fields. Mendel's model used as its category the abstract notion of *genetic factor*. Later a "reduction of category" occurred when the *genetic factors* were identified as material structures—genes. The models of organic evolution began with generalities and became more specific as knowledge of genetics advanced. The evolutionary model demoted man from his assumed status at the center of creation as the Copernican model had demoted the earth from an assumed status at the center of the universe.

The Freudian model of human behavior also illustrated a development from an abstract set of factors, the *id*, *ego*, and *superego*, to a material model insofar as the factors can be identified with physiological structure. A curious anticipation of this model is noted in Bacon's *idols* of the *Novum Organum*.

Chapter XIII

Models in Social Science

Magic. Taboo. Names. Theories of history: Hegel, Marx, Spengler, Toynbee. Theory of games. Linear programming. Operations research. Beauty.

Anthropologists have contributed to science a model which is basic to the understanding of science and its place in society. They did not invent this model; rather, they exhumed it during their study of primitive cultures of the past and present. This model is the theory of nature which is implicit in the practice of primitive *magic*. Primitive man was trying to survive, and magic was one of his survival techniques. By magic he tried to control nature for his own benefit. The control of nature of course implies predictability. Primitive men did not verbalize their postulates, but anthropologists have inferred their postulates from their practice. These postulates are:

(1) Nature is orderly and uniform.
(2) The same cause always produces the same effect unless the cause is interfered with.
(3) Things which have been in intimate contact retain an intimate relationship when they are separated.
(4) Animate and inanimate objects can be controlled by manipulating other objects which resemble them.
(5) The name of a thing is part of it, and control of the name confers control over the thing.

Postulate (1) at first glance seems surprising because primitive man conveys the impression that "anything can happen" in his world. However, his practice of magic shows clearly that he regards the world as an automatic machine; if he can once find the proper magic, then he can bring rain or keep it away, cause his own crops to prosper and those of his enemy to wither. Even when he regards the rain as controlled by a rain god, the proper magic will make the rain god behave. Nature and gods are alike subject to law; the man who knows the right magic can control them. There is a saying in India, "The whole universe is subject to the gods; the gods are subject to the mantras [Vedic hymns]; the mantras are subject to the Brahmans; therefore the Brahmans are our gods." Humility is not an outstanding characteristic of man.

Postulate (2) explains why this model has lasted for thousands of years. The rain dance always causes rain; if rain does not come it is because the dance was improper or because an enemy has danced the rain away again. This intuition is not to be despised. Many a scientific model has been eventually validated by a scientist who explained his predictive failures by assuming his rain dance was not accurate or powerful enough.

Postulates (3) and (4) are often combined. A picture of deer near the water hole will bring deer to the water hole, especially if the paint has been mixed with deer fat and the picture drawn with a deer bone. An image of your enemy can be tortured and destroyed, thereby causing pain and death to the enemy, but only if the image contains hair, fingernails, or other intimate parts of that enemy. The careful man does not leave parts of himself to become available for such uses.

Postulate (5) seems strange and alien to us nowadays, but the notion is universal among primitive people. The concept presumably dates back to the beginning of language, and conveys to us something of the wonder and power that words had in the beginning. This feeling developed eventually into the concept of the *Logos*, an idea that seems to be a mixture of equal parts of the ideas of language, reason, God, and mystery. The ability to distinguish the name from the thing is a sophisticated attainment, and in some types of mental disease the patient loses that ability.

A primitive man often keeps his own name secret, even from other members of his own tribe. The Hebrew tribes would not pronounce the name of their god lest someone hear it and thereby gain control over the god. The resentment a modern man feels when a near-stranger addresses him by his first name is perhaps a faint echo of the fear of our remote ancestors. In the book of Genesis, man is permitted to *name* the animals, thereby giving him control over them.

Taboo is the negative side of magic. Sprinkling water on the garden will bring rain—ask any gardener. If you don't want rain, then sprinkling is *taboo*. If you want to be extremely careful, avoid spilling water while drinking; you may turn on the rain accidentally. Magic controls the levers which control nature; taboo is the avoidance of the lever which turns on an unwanted event.

The nature model of modern science is a modification of the nature model of magic. As usual, the successful parts of the model have been retained. Postulates (1) and (2) are part of our current models. Postulates (3), (4), and (5) have been discarded as universal principles but have left residues. Observations on identical twins show occurrences which remind one of postulate (3). Designers of manual-control devices and "tell-tales" for airplanes and submarines find postulate (4) useful in trying to capitalize on man's instinctive behavior tendencies for use during emergency. Postulate (5) has developed into a whole area of research, the field of *semantics*.

We turn now from the fields of anthropology and sociology to the related field of history. It is likely that the systematic study of history arose from the hero tales and legends which abound in all societies. Men have always delighted in such tales, and this pleasure is another example of nature's providing an immediate emotional reward for a practice which tends to assist survival. Legends and hero tales are stories of how our ancestors used their wits, their strength, and their knowledge to survive under difficulties. The listeners are learning two things—the technique of survival under adversity, and the more subtle indoctrination that man is the most indomitable animal ever evolved by nature in the known universe. As man's behavior changed from instinctive survival patterns to conscious survival patterns, it became obvious that a knowledge of history—the triumphs and mistakes of our ancestors—provided predictive knowledge valuable for survival.

Two examples of predictive models in history will be given. All history carries some implication of predictive use, but explicit attempts to predict the future of nations and cultures are rarer. Hegel's philosophy of history is predictive only in a vague and general sort of way. A more specific attempt to be predictive occurs in the dialectical philosophy of Karl Marx (1818–1883), but here also detailed predictions are not attempted.

The first impressive example of a predictive model in history is that described by Oswald Spengler (1880–1936) in his book *The Decline of the West.* * Spengler constructed a model of portions of world history by comparing the history of certain periods and peoples to the birth, growth, and decay of an organism. He tabulated six of these sociological organisms during the course of world history: Egyptian (3400 B.C.), Chinese (1700 B.C.), Classical (1600 B.C.), Indian (1500 B.C.), Arabian (500 B.C.), Western (A.D. 500). Each date shows the approximate beginning of the precultural period. Spengler also discusses without tabulation a Babylonian and a Mexican culture.

Each organism exhibits three stages: preculture, culture, and civilization, and the latter two are divided into several epochs. The corresponding epochs of the eight organisms display a remarkable homologism in art, literature, architecture, music, mathematics, science, philosophy, and theology.

The beginning of a culture is characterized by a rural and feudal economy, a spoken literature of hero tales, and an uncritical acceptance of the gods. Later culture is characterized by urban communities governed by economic power. Theology and philosophy are rationalistic; art, mathematics, and science flourish. Then comes the stage of civilization; the megalopolis appears with its masses, and enormous architectural structures are built. It is an age of Caesarism and wars of annihilation, an age of materialism and pragmatism. Technology flourishes, but there is no creativity in art, literature, or science. Great men are things of the past. In its final stage, as civilization crumbles before some outer or inner attack, there appears a *second religiousness*, an attempt to return to the theology of the cultural springtime.

The twentieth century finds Western culture in the stage of megalopolitan

* Oswald Spengler, *The Decline of the West* (New York: Alfred A. Knopf, Inc., 1945).

civilization. The future contains for us only a steady decline. Spengler, who conceived the model before 1914 and published it in 1918, allowed about two hundred years for the extent of Western civilization, hence the apt title of his book, *Der Untergang des Abendlandes* ("The Going-Under of the Evening-Land").

The extent of validation to be accorded this model is controversial. There has been extensive criticism of the postdictions of the model, and its predictions remain to be checked by future events. The creativity of the twentieth century in science has been greater than Spengler predicted; the extent of creativity in art, literature, and music is more difficult to judge. The political predictions of the model seem to be quite accurate so far. The value of Spengler's model lies in its boldness of conception as an example to historians of the possibility of predictive models in history.

A second example of a predictive model in history occurs in the works of Arnold Toynbee. In his *Study of History*, he modified extensively the Spenglerian model.[*] The basic unit of the Toynbee model is the *society*. Out of a society there may come a *civilization* which appears, develops, breaks down, and dies. Toynbee distinguishes twenty-eight civilizations during the course of world history. Of these, eighteen are dead, nine have broken down, and only one, our own, *Western Christendom*, is still vigorous.

A civilization comes into being when a society encounters a *challenge* and succeeds in overcoming the problem. The marshes and jungles of the Nile challenged the inhabitants, and from their response arose the Egyptian civilization. The climate of the far North and its geography challenged the Eskimo society and produced a skillful technology, but the problem was so great that no civilization developed. The easy climate of Nyasaland provided no challenge, and the inhabitants remained primitive.

The growth of a civilization originates with creative individuals or small minorities; the process of *mimesis*, imitation of the external form, transfers the inspiration to the masses. Political and military expansion do not indicate growth. Real progress is indicated by successful response to internal spiritual challenge. Breakdown occurs when the creative powers of the minority fail, and the masses withdraw their allegiance. The society breaks into three parts, and each part develops a specific product. The uncreative minority retains dominance by political power and a universal state is produced. The internal proletariat achieve a universal church, and the external proletariat produce barbarian bands which war against the state.

Western Christendom has not yet produced a universal state. The internal proletariat as yet shows no evidence of evolving a universal church. Toynbee does not suggest it, but faith in science may correspond to the universal church in this civilization. Our civilization has exhausted the supply of external barbarians, and has bred its own as in the pagan cults of Nazi Germany.

Historians have been very critical of both Spengler's and Toynbee's

[*] Arnold Toynbee, *A Study of History* (New York: Oxford University Press, 1934–1954).

attempts to construct models of history. The critical test of the validity of any model is the accuracy of its predictions. The models of history developed thus far permit only long-range, general predictions, and not enough time has elapsed to permit a conviction of either validation or invalidation.

We turn now to a particular aspect of history, economic factors, and discuss a certain model in the field of economics. The models of economics can be represented by the mathematical model described by John von Neumann (1903–1957) and Oskar Morgenstern in *The Theory of Games and Economic Behavior.**

The science of economics appears to be at a stage of development analogous to that of physics at the time of Galileo. No Tycho Brahe of economics has yet appeared to gather accurate data in an organized fashion, and this lack prevents an economic Johann Kepler from formulating empirical laws. It would be premature to try to construct a general economic model at this stage. Rather, one should try to isolate some simple, perhaps trivial, aspect of economics and attempt to construct a rigorous model of this single aspect. By analogy to physical science, it is likely that a form of mathematics peculiarly suitable to economics will need to be developed before more general models are feasible. Thus Newton and others had to develop the infinitesimal calculus before mechanics could appear, and Fourier series had to be developed before a general theory of heat was possible. At this stage of physics a rigorous model of the behavior of a falling object was formulated; in economics one might hope to solve an equally basic problem.

Morgenstern and von Neumann approach the problem by regarding economic behavior as a game of strategy played by a large number of players, where each player tries to behave so as to maximize his winnings. The procedure is to construct first a model of games between two players, then proceed to three players, and so on to n players, where n may be a large number. At first they consider *zero-sum* games, where the amount won by a single player exactly equals the amount lost by the others. Later they are able to show that a zero-sum game for n players is a special case of a nonzero-sum game for $n + 1$ players. The type of mathematics applicable turns out to be mostly *theory of sets.*

The Morgenstern-von Neumann (MvN) model requires that a player possess a clear intuition whether he prefers event A to a combination of probable events B and C, where B may occur with probability P and, if B does not occur, C may occur with probability $(1 - P)$. It is certain that B or C will occur, but the relative frequency is measured by $P/(1 - P)$.

As an illustration, ten bags are prepared and numbered; the first contains one red marble and nine yellow marbles, the second bag contains two red marbles and eight yellow, and so on. A player must know whether he prefers to be given one green marble, or to be given the opportunity to draw one marble from, say, the third bag.

---

* J. von Neumann and Oskar Morgenstern, *The Theory of Games and Economic Behavior* (Princeton, N.J.: Princeton University Press, 1955).

A *play* (of a game) is a finite sequence of *moves*, where each *move* is a choice among a number of alternatives. A *personal move* is one which is decided by a choice made by the player; a *chance move* is one specified, for example, by a mechanical device (say a throw of dice) which operates according to a probability law. At each move a player has available a definite amount of information. The amount depends on the rules of the game, and may vary from zero to a complete knowledge of all previous moves. The rules of the game also specify how each player is to be rewarded at the end of the *play*.

A game may be formalized set-theoretically by specifying mathematical entities such as the following:

(1) Each play of a game is specified by a sequence of numbers S. Each number S_k specifies the choice among the possible alternatives for move k.

(2) All possible sequences S for different plays of a game constitute the finite set Z which characterizes that game.

(3) For each player m, there is a function $F_m(S)$ depending on the sequence of moves which specifies the winnings of the mth player for that specific play S.

(4) At each move k of a play, there is a set A_k which specifies all choices made prior to move k. Set A_k is the information available to an umpire who has recorded all choices made during the play up to move k.

These four statements constitute part of the MvN model of elementary economic behavior. The theory is developed rigorously up through the five-person game. Numerous predictions are made concerning the conduct of specific games, and no invalidation has yet appeared.

In planning activities to maximize the economic gain, it is sometimes possible to express the gain as a linear function of selling price, cost of materials, cost of labor, and other such parameters. These parameters will usually also be involved in subsidiary equations which constrain their values. The maximization of linear equations subject to linear constraint equations predicts the optimum choice of the variables; this procedure is called *linear programming*. If the equations involved are quadratic, the procedure is *quadratic programming*, and so on.

The application of mathematics to economics and games of strategy suggested the use of quantitative methods for guiding decisions of policy in war and business. *Operations research* is the name for such activity. An operations research group (ORG) is typically a group of mathematical, scientific, and technical experts charged with the responsibility of giving technical advice to a commanding officer. In order that an ORG may be able to operate objectively, the ORG itself has neither the authority nor the responsibility for making decisions. The actual decisions are made by the military commander or company executive using as much or as little of the advice from the ORG as he chooses. Operations research was used extensively and effectively by the United States military forces during the war of 1941–1945, and many large companies have used such methods during the last thirty years. Operations research is an outstanding example of scientific prediction as a survival technique.

The final model to be considered in this chapter concerns itself with the sensation of *beauty*. Many writers have considered that man's love of beauty is a phenomenon safely beyond any materialistic model of man. However, such a judgment appears to be premature. It has been remarked that the sensation of pleasure arising from eating, mating, and other activities necessary to survival is nature's method of immediately rewarding acts which have a delayed contribution to survival. Eating contributes vigor only after a delay of several hours when digestion is complete. Mating is a negative contribution to survival until the children are old enough to help defend the parents. Yet eating is necessary for personal survival, and mating is necessary for species survival. The animal which lacks a mechanism for providing the sensation of pleasure immediately and memorably will survive only briefly.

Experiments with rats have located this pleasure mechanism in the brain. When this region is stimulated electrically, the rat reacts as though he found the sensation pleasurable. If the stimulus is so arranged that the rat can provide it for himself by pushing a lever, he soon learns to do so. The rat will continue to push the lever repeatedly without stopping for food or sleep until he is exhausted. Clearly, the pleasure that normally rewards some act that has survival value (perhaps eating or mating) is now being provided merely by pushing a pedal without the necessity of performing the act itself. With the help of man, the rat has tricked nature into paying a reward without exacting the usual service.

The sensation of beauty arises when a sense stimulus from an object or situation which once contributed to survival acts directly on the pleasure center of the brain. Man learned to associate bright colors with flowers and fruits which provided food. Now the colors, even in a painting, give him pleasure directly. Landscapes which were associated with peace and plenty came to provide pleasure directly. Noises which were associated with pleasant occasions eventually stimulated the pleasure centers directly; the reed flute of the wedding feast became the symphony orchestra, which gives pleasure directly without assistance from food or bride.

The enjoyment of beauty is a short circuit in nature's wiring, but it does not follow that such enjoyment is a threat to survival. Provided that the enjoyment does not interfere with other necessary survival acts, it is not only harmless but may contribute to survival in an indirect way. A combat pilot may listen to music between flights and be all the more alert when he is on duty; the composer of the music and the entire orchestra have helped to defend their society. Art, music, and literature are not only the fruits of civilization but contributions to its survival.

Argument

Primitive man tried to control nature by means of *magic*. Inherent in the practice of magic is the assumption that nature is orderly and controllable. Even primitive man had a large stock of empirical knowledge of his world, and he used this knowledge, sometimes deliberately, sometimes unconsciously, to make the predictions which were man's specific survival technique from the earliest times. Magic was man's first conscious effort to control nature for his own ends. The postulates inherent in the practice of magic now seem naïve, but they represent man's first strivings toward the abstractions and generalizations which are the building material of conscious scientific thought. Magic was the forerunner of formal science.

All history carries some implication of predictive use, but most historians have not attempted to predict explicitly the future of nations and cultures. Models of history designed especially for predictive use have been constructed by Hegel, Marx, Spengler, and Toynbee; the models of the latter two are described briefly. These models all permit only long-range, general predictions, and not enough time has yet elapsed to permit validation or invalidation of any model.

The beginnings of a mathematical model of economics have been developed by von Neumann and Morgenstern, and this model is described briefly. The quantitative methods used for guiding decisions of policy in war and business are known as *operations research*. This field of thought has developed rapidly over the last thirty years and will very likely become a dominant feature of future societies.

Acts which make a delayed contribution to survival are rewarded immediately by a feeling of pleasure. The mechanism which produces the sensation of pleasure may be triggered directly; if this occurs, the organism receives the reward sensation without performing the survival act. The sensation of beauty (for example) arises when a sense stimulus from an object or situation which once contributed to survival now acts directly on the appropriate pleasure center of the brain. This process will not be a threat to survival unless it interferes with necessary routine activity, and in many cases the process contributes indirectly to survival.

Chapter XIV

Science and Ethics

Physical and moral law. Anthropomorphic models. Description and verbot. Historic models of moral law. Narrative form of models. Validation by experience. Sensation accompanying discovery of physical and moral law. Illumination. Tension between science and theology. Mysticism in the church. Authority of nature. Survival not a choice. Rational and moral behavior. Original sin. Free will. Responsibility. Survival of personality. Religion as survival technique.

Man has attempted to survive as an individual and as a species by using the scientific method to predict the future. A rational man then bases his behavior on these predictions. Science may thus be regarded as a source of advice regarding behavior although the advice is not given explicitly and must be inferred from the predictions.

Ethics is also a source of advice regarding behavior, and ethical advice is given directly: "Thou shalt not steal!" This essay will attempt to show that the advice given by science and ethics has the same origin, the same purpose, and the same degree of reliability. The origin is human experience; the purpose is human survival; and the reliability is not very great, but it is fairly adequate for the purpose, and, in any event, it is all the reliability man can attain from any source.

Some writers distinguish between the word *moral*, referring to how a culture does behave, and *ethical*, referring to how a culture thinks it ought to behave. This essay will make no distinction between these words and will use them interchangeably. However, this usage does not imply that there is no distinction between what a culture actually does and what it thinks it ought to do.

Ethical statements give advice on behavior. This advice always assumes a desired end although this end is very seldom stated. Many writers on ethics start with two postulates: (1) there exists a pattern of behavior which may be called "ideal ethical behavior"; (2) every human being ought to strive toward this ideal behavior as much as he can. The exact form of this ideal pattern is not known in its entirety, but there is enough agreement about the pattern so that ethical teachers of widely different cultures often give very similar advice. The origin of man's alleged knowledge of this ideal ethical behavior has been the subject of much discussion. Some ethical teachers have believed that such knowledge came to them by direct revelation from God. For many of these teachers, God is an existing supernatural person and ethical behavior consists of doing the will of God. This essay will reverse that order. The pattern of ideal ethical behavior will be inferred from experience, and the concept of God will be regarded as a personification of that ideal pattern. This point of view will require a reinterpretation of statements made by various ethical teachers.

Some ethical teachers have based their rules on intuition; others have sought to derive their rules from postulated general principles. These proposed sources are not convincing, as indicated by the number and variety of different attempts to base ethics upon them.

A number of writers in the field of ethics have concerned themselves with propositional functions of the form, "X is good," where X represents a word specifying an act or course of action. The resulting groups of words are complete sentences, but it is doubtful if any verifiable meaning can be attached to them. In order to attach a verifiable meaning to "X is good," one must assume it is an abbreviation for the more complete sentence, "X is good for the purpose of attaining end Y under conditions Z." One might assume that "X is good" means "X is good for the purpose of attaining any end Y under any conditions Z." There would not appear to be any such X, so no occasion would arise where "X is good" would have a verifiable meaning. If one assumes with Aristotle that there is a unique end Y which may be regarded as the ultimate aim of all actions, it still seems unlikely that there is any X which would favor the attainment of Y under all circumstances. Finally one might assume that "X is good" means "X is good for the purpose of attaining many ends under many conditions." Such an interpretation seems too vague to be useful in trying to classify a proposed action.

The complete form is actually a prediction: "I predict that X will be found good for the purpose of attaining end Y under conditions Z." This prediction can be tested in the same way as any other prediction; try it and see. Ethical statements are sentences which advise certain behavior. The ends Y and the conditions Z are often omitted, but they are consciously or unconsciously presumed by the writer, and must be provided by the reader if the sentence is to have any verifiable meaning.

Hans Reichenbach (1891–1953) wrote that science can advise man how to attain an end, but science cannot tell man whether he ought to choose that end. This essay points out that there is one end—survival of man as an individual and as a species—that man does not have to choose. It is a matter of observation that man does in fact try to act so as to maximize his probability of survival as individual and species. If he is observed to be taking his own life or the lives of others who are no threat to him, he is classed as insane or the victim of misinformation. Such individuals are rare and tend to eliminate their own type from the population. The basic choice "to be or not to be" was made for living things at their creation. This common purpose of all men is the ultimate motivation of all normal behavior. The Christian martyr is pursuing the same end; he seeks his particular variety of survival—eternal life in heaven—for himself and all mankind. The hero who gives his life for his society does so because he feels that his act will increase the probability of survival of those who share his ideals, his recommended behavior for his species.

This essay will infer advice from the following definition: ethical behavior for man is that pattern of individual and collective conduct which maximizes the probability of survival of man as individual and species. This definition permits an act to be classified as ethical or unethical by examining its consequences. As time goes on and consequences become clearer, the classification of a given act in the past may change. The nuclear bombing of Hiroshima, which was intended as an ethical act (to save the lives, both Japanese and American, which would be lost in a full-scale invasion), may be classified as unethical by future historians. A classification is never certain because man is not omniscient. A man must judge whether an act is ethical or unethical in advance, hence he must try to predict the consequences. He extrapolates his knowledge of the past to predict the future. This procedure is the domain of science. His classification of acts as ethical or unethical is as reliable as his scientific predictions of future events, no more and no less. Some ethical judgments will be as "certain" as, "The sun will rise tomorrow"; others will be as uncertain as, "The probability of rain tomorrow is three out of ten."

This definition of *ethical behavior* is operationally equivalent to the traditional statement that ethical behavior is conduct according to the will of God. Religious tradition has it that God created man, encouraged him to be fruitful, and forbade suicide. Thus a pattern of behavior which maximizes man's survival is at least part of the will of God as traditionally accepted. The possibility still remains that behavior to encourage survival is not all that is necessary. It is assumed here that such items as courtesy and loving kindness, which at first appear to be optional, are positive contributions to survival probability and hence are included in the definition of ethical conduct. From this point of view the behavior of such societies as Nazi Germany does not maximize their probability of survival and leads eventually to their destruction.

Mathematicians will inquire how two different quantities, probability of individual survival and probability of species survival, can be maximized simultaneously. The quantity to be maximized is the sum of the weighted probabilities. The weighting factors must be estimated from empirical observation bearing in mind that the weighting factors have changed in the past and will probably change in the future. Different species at the present time weight the factors quite differently. Among bees and ants the survival of the species appears to be heavily weighted.

Ethical predictions take a long time to test empirically, and observations must be extended over many generations. The ethical advice, "Honor thy father and thy mother," according to tradition was pronounced by Moses acting as spokesman for the God of the Hebrews. In this case the end is stated: ". . . that thy days may be long. . . ." The conditions are not stated, but we must infer a set of conditions if the statement is to be verifiable. The assumed consitions will specify the procedure necessary for verification. Let us assume that Moses was talking to the Hebrews and that he had in mind the general conditions of Hebrew life. A predictive form of the commandment is then: "I [Moses] predict that those Hebrews who honor their fathers and mothers will increase their probability of living a long time."

This prediction is clearly based on tribal experience handed down by legend. Primitive tribes had little regard for old people; when men and women became too old to look out for themselves, they were left behind to starve when the tribe migrated. The commandment is saying, "If you honor and look after your old parents, you are setting an example for your son to follow when you yourself get old." This example illustrates clearly the concern for continued survival and the fact that obedience to this law automatically brings a probability of reward.

The shortening of an ethical rule to a simple verbot is quite common in our own society. The sign "No Passing" on a highway is an abbreviation for, "If you pass on this part of the highway, it is predicted that the probability of your survival and that of other people is decreased." This is an empirical rule; our society accepts its validity and attempts to enforce it. Intelligent individuals obey it except when unusual conditions (for example, an emergency trip to the hospital) change the probabilities so that other behavior becomes preferable. One "takes a chance" in order to increase the probability of survival of the patient.

The forms of expression of models of the physical law and models of the moral law are today quite different. Models of physical laws are often expressed mathematically. For example, the second law of Newton states that if one applies a net force F to a body of mass M, the acceleration of the body is equal to F divided by M. Models of the moral law have a statistical form. The eighth law of Moses, for example, says, "Thou shalt not steal." This is an abbreviation for, "Stealing decreases the probability of survival of man as individual and species." Most societies feel that the empirical evidence for such a law is convincing and try to enhance their probability of survival by punishing those who transgress. Since an individual's probability of survival often depends on his possessions, he is quite willing to cooperate with public opinion by punishing the person who steals.

The prevalence of the verbot form of models of ethical laws has produced the illusion that there is a difference between natural laws and ethical laws. The difference is commonly stated in this way: a man can disobey the ethical law, "Thou shalt not steal," by committing a theft, but a man cannot disobey Newton's second law by any action whatever. This apparent difference disappears immediately when one regards "Thou shalt not steal" as an abbreviation for "Stealing decreases the probability of survival of man as individual and species." This form corresponds closely to "Application of the force F to the mass M produces the acceleration F divided by M." A man may or may not apply the force F, but if he does, then the specified acceleration occurs. Similarly, a man may or may not steal, but if he does, then the specified decrease in probability occurs. The fact that the numerical value of the decrease is not specified in this ethical law is not an essential difference from physical law. Many physical laws predict only the direction of a change without specifying its magnitude.

Ethical teachers have attributed their knowledge to revelation, intuition, and the exercise of pure reason. This essay considers that, consciously or unconsciously, the source of their statements were observations of man as individual and society. These observations and simple predictions from them often took the form of myth, legend, proverb, aphorism, and written and verbal history. Such a point of view need not offend the religious person, for God could make use of all of these means to convey His desires to His prophets; and the prophets would be entirely accurate in attributing their knowledge to God. Scientific and ethical models are, in themselves, never religious or irreligious. Any model can be interpreted by the religious person as describing the means which God used to attain his ends; the same model can be used by others without mention of God. Aquinas to the contrary, the existence of God cannot be proved or disproved by reason or experience, by mathematics or science.

An attempt might be made to base ethical classification on the maximization of probability of individual survival alone. It seems obvious that the probability of individual survival would be increased by an individual behavior which showed concern for the survival of others of his species. This essay does not adopt that postulate because it leads to a classification contradictory to the teaching of many ethical thinkers. Consider a man who does not believe in an afterlife, but "voluntarily" becomes a martyr to aid the survival of others of his society. Ethical teachers tend to regard this act as moral even when they have little approval for the society itself. The individual survival postulate would classify this act as unethical. The empiricist respects the judgments of many ethical teachers because he considers that these judgments are insights based on observation of society. This essay considers that the postulate of maximization of probability of survival of individual and species gives greater correspondence to the consensus of ethical teachers.

On the other hand, one might attempt to base ethical classification on the maximization of probability of species survival alone. Some insect societies appear to approach this procedure. Its success is probably due to the fact that an individual insect is not very imaginative and does not worry about his own individual future. Man, however, is very imaginative and does worry about his individual future. It seems likely that an ethic which required a man to subordinate completely his own powerful drive toward personal survival to concern for species survival alone would lead to such low morale that the survival probability of the species would be decreased by such a policy. The adoption of the postulate specifying maximization of the weighted sum of the probabilities of personal and species survival permits one to adjust the weighting factors to give maximum correspondence to the observed conditions for each species.

The procedures of science and ethics not only run parallel; they are basically the same procedure. In science one assumes the existence of an external world predictable by natural law, observes it quantitatively, and builds models to postdict and predict observations. The procedure which yields correct prediction is called a *model of the natural law*. For ethics one assumes the existence of a pattern of behavior of man which provides the maximum probability for the survival of man as individual and species. One then observes the behavior of man as individual and society, and attempts to build models which will predict successfully the probability of survival of the individual and the species. The pattern of behavior which promises maximum probability of survival may be called a *model of the moral law*.

When men first started building models of the natural law, these models were often anthropomorphic. The wind, the lightning, and other natural phenomena were explained by the behavior of nature gods. The early models of the moral law were also anthropomorphic, and wars, epidemics, and other social phenomena were explained by the favor or disfavor of tribal gods.

Early examples of models of the natural law and models of the moral law exist in all ancient literatures. The same model often contained a confused mixture of the two types. Our present-day abstractions of physicist, sociologist, theologian, and the like are not easily applicable to these early thinkers; several of these activities were often combined in one man. The Greeks, who had a particular genius for study of the natural law, called such a man a *philosopher*, a lover of knowledge. The Hebrews, who had a particular genius for study of the moral law, called such a man a *prophet*, that is, one who speaks for God, the personification of the moral law. The philosopher was careful to say that his words were not merely his own, but were dictated by the law of the universe. The prophet also indicated that his words were not his own, but were his pronouncement of the will of God, of the judgment of the moral law.

The writer of Chapters II and III of the book of Genesis combined the viewpoint of the cosmologist, the sociologist, and the theologian within one person. His model (received about 1300 B.C., published about 800 B.C.) described the origin of the universe and of man. The model explained why man had to work hard, why women were subject to men, why childbirth was painful, why snakes had no legs, and a variety of other biological and social phenomena known to him. Doubtless he combined into one masterly model the contributions of his predecessors and his own genius. In his society, women were of little account, and his model shows her created as an afterthought when the rest of creation was finished. A second and later writer (about 500 B.C.) had a higher opinion of women, and his model (Genesis, Chapter I) creates her along with man on the sixth day of creation.

These early models are often in narrative form, and, in fact, the form of narrative or parable seems as intrinsically appropriate to models of the moral law as mathematics is appropriate to models of the physical law. The early models confused the physical and moral laws, and the fire god of the primitive Hebrews who exacted human sacrifice was confused with the moral god who taught them to do no murder. The model is modified in the narrative of Abraham and Isaac (Genesis, Chapter XXII), where Abraham decides that God cannot possibly desire human sacrifice, and offers instead a lamb. The model is modified again and animal sacrifice forbidden when Amos, speaking for the moral law, thunders: "Thus says the Lord . . . I hate, I despise your feasts . . . Even though you offer me your burnt offerings . . . I will not accept them . . . But let justice roll down like waters and righteousness like an overflowing stream."

Some 800 years later came one who said, "Think not that I have come to destroy the law and the prophets: I am not come to destroy but to fulfill . . . You have heard that it hath been said, thou shalt love thy neighbor and hate thine enemy . . . but I say unto you . . . love your enemies." Here again is the model of the moral law modified, and the successful parts of the old model are included in the new. The test of a model of the moral law is the same as the test of a model of the physical law, namely, empirical observation. A model of the natural law is validated by successful prediction. A model of the moral law is validated by its prescription of a behavior which leads to a stable and comfortable society. A model which leads to a corrupt society, one which will obviously not endure, is a false model and its protagonist, a false prophet. "Beware of false prophets . . . ye shall know them by their fruits."

The similarity of experience of those who study mathematics or science, the natural law, and those who study the moral law is shown by a comparison of two books: *The Psychology of Invention in the Mathematical Field* by Jacques Hadamard* and *The Varieties of Religious Experience* by William James.† Hadamard is reporting the extension of a study started by Henri Poincaré which was suggested by a personal experience with mathematical invention. Poincaré had been studying a problem involving a certain class of functions (later called *Fuchsian* functions), and had had little success. He felt like one trying to map a dark valley by groping around in it and trying to imagine how it would look in the daylight. Other affairs intervened, and he was forced to give up all conscious attention to the problem. Some time later, as Poincaré was boarding an omnibus with a friend, the solution of the problem came to him instantly. It was as though he were standing on a mountain overlooking the dark valley, which was illuminated for an instant by a flash of lightning. In that instant the whole problem became clear to him, although it took him many weeks to write down and derive all the relations.

If Poincaré had been a mystic, he would have regarded the event as a

* Jacques Hadamard, *The Psychology of Invention in the Mathematical Field* (New York: Dover Publications, 1954).

† William James, *The Varieties of Religious Experience* (New York: Modern Library, 1902).

revelation; actually, he ascribed the occurrence to his subconscious mind, which he believed had continued to work on the problem after the conscious mind was otherwise engaged. The occurrence was so vivid that he wrote to some forty other mathematicians and learned that many of them had undergone a similar experience. It later developed that men involved in creative work in many fields had encountered the same sort of event. Valéry had experienced it while writing poetry, Langevin while solving problems in physics, Ostwald while studying chemistry, Mozart while writing music, Schweitzer while pondering ethics. . . . Many of them compared the occurrence to a blinding flash of light.

Turning now to *The Varieties of Religious Experience*, we find the same pattern. Men ponder moral and religious questions for long periods, and then suddenly undergo an experience that can only be described as an *illumination* or *photism*. The event is almost always compared to a great light. Being mystics, these men ascribe their experience to a revelation, and the experience is utterly convincing.

The conclusion is inescapable that the act of creation or discovery in the human mind is associated with the sensation of light. The comparison has even become a part of the language, and one speaks of having a "bright idea"; a smart child is a "bright" child. The convention of the cartoonist indicates the arrival of an idea by a glowing lamp bulb.

Searching through ancient Hebrew literature, one finds many examples of the illumination accompanying the birth of a new model. At the coming of the decalogue the mountain is bathed by great lightnings; when the moral law guides Moses to lead the Hebrews out of Egypt, God speaks from out the light of the burning bush. When the Hebrews are in the wilderness, they are guided by a pillar of fire. The confusion between the fire god of the primitive tribes and the illumination of the moral law is no accident, for they are aspects of the same thing. In the psalms of the Hebrews, light is the greatest aspect of God, and those without Him "walk in darkness."

The great example of illumination and discovery is the experience of Paul on the road to Damascus. Paul, an ardent member of the strict Jewish sect of Pharisees, had been persecuting the Christians with great fervor and obtained official authorization to extend his efforts to Damascus. "Now as he journeyed he approached Damascus, and suddenly a light from heaven flashed about him and he fell to the ground and heard a voice saying . . . 'Why do you persecute me?'" Paul was converted in this instant and became one of the great Christian protagonists.

Clearly the human brain reacts in much the same way whether it is studying the moral law or the natural law. The state of tension between science and theology is caused by a different preference for categories. The scientist prefers materialistic and mathematical categories; the theologian prefers the mystical and poetic categories of religion. Scientists have learned by humiliating experience that their model is not reality. Theologians still labor under the illusion that their model *is* reality, and fear any change because changes are hard to reconcile with such ultimate knowledge. The religious-minded have a desperate hunger for the forbidden fruits of the Garden of Eden: knowledge of ultimate reality and life everlasting.

The various Christian churches of the world have in common a supernatural theology which few scientists can bring themselves to accept. If this supernaturalism is accepted as vital to Christianity, the scientists must become Sunday mystics or ignore the church entirely. However, natural theology provides an adequate basis for the Church; theologians since the first century have contributed little but dissension.

The synoptic gospels show that the founder of Christianity stressed two things: love for God and love for neighbor. His teaching was directed toward the creation of a kingdom of God, on earth, and within the lifetime of His disciples. The only prayer we have from Him asked for but three things: daily bread, the coming of the kingdom on earth, and forgiveness. There is no reference to eschatology, and He disclaimed knowledge of it. The Christian church is departing from the path followed by its founder when it adds anything to these teachings. The scientist should remain in his church and teach it; if he has studied the evidence, his inferences and thought processes are at least as reliable as the inferences and thought processes of the theologians.

The attitude of the scientist toward authority is often misunderstood, and becomes a source of confusion in communicating with those in other disciplines. The scientist recognizes no authority except an empirical observation of nature. In practice he will sometimes accept a report of such an observation by a careful researcher, but in general a consensus of several researchers is preferred.

The scientist insists that students work in the laboratory to teach them this attitude toward authority. Newton's second law is taught, not because Newton said it was accurate, or because the textbook says so, or because the instructor says so, but because the student can go into the laboratory and verify its accuracy. The intelligent student never has any difficulty with errors of measurement or other extraneous items which some intentionally obtuse writers quote as vitiating the process. The student seldom verifies any law very accurately, and never verifies all laws, but he does become convinced that empirical observation is the ultimate court of appeal which can be invoked if necessary for any statement or law of his science.

This attitude toward authority prevents the scientist from accepting the religious interpretation of mystical experiences. William James reports that those undergoing such experiences find the religious interpretation completely convincing, but presumably the scientist would not. He has been trained to distrust his own personal experiences and emotions. He would freely admit that he had experienced a subjective psychological occurrence. By studying the records he would find many cases of other obviously competent and honest people who had reported experiences which were essentially the same as his own. But here the scientist departs from the path of the mystic, and the categories he uses to "explain" the experience are essentially materialistic. The mystics' easy acceptance of an explanation with no possibility of empirical validation puzzles the scientist. Such an acceptance is impossible for him, and he can only conclude that the mystic has never encountered the feeling of conviction which the scientist finds in empirical validation. The mystic presumably concludes that the scientist has never encountered the feeling of conviction which the mystic finds in his interpretation of his own experience. Impasse.

The drive for personal survival in normally functioning organisms can only be overcome by the drive for species survival. When this occurs, it is the automatic result of current conditions acting on the personal and social experience of the organism. The sensation of choice is merely an awareness of the automatic functioning of the nervous system. The drive for survival is so intense that it often overrides the logical operation of the brain, and many men adopt doctrines which promise eternal survival despite almost infinite evidence to the contrary.

Rational behavior consists in being guided by the predictions of the most successful known model of natural law. Moral behavior consists in being guided by the predictions of the most successful known model of the moral law. No man can ever predict with certainty all of the consequences of his act; he must act according to the knowledge available to him at the time. Hence an act which seemed moral in 1945 may seem immoral in 1955 and by 1965 again appear moral.

Even in simple situations where the consequences of an act seem fairly predictable, a man does not always behave in a way to maximize the probability of survival of himself and his species. A concern for the survival of others is a fairly recent evolutionary development. For hundreds of millions of years our remote ancestors—the protozoa and their descendants —were concerned only with personal survival. Only in the last few million years have our ancestors begun to defend their young and their mates. The survival value of defending a neighbor has become clear only in the last few thousand years. A man's behavior is influenced by his environment, his stored memories, and his heredity. Moral behavior requires that a man concern himself with species survival as well as personal survival. A father must decide whether to defend his family or to abandon it; a soldier must decide whether to support his company or to run away. There is a great desire to revert to the ways of our remote ancestors, who concerned themselves only with personal survival. This innate tendency to revert to egocentricity has haunted man's history, and has received a spectacular name: *original sin.*

It is a common assumption that a man is free to choose among several possible courses of action. Is this assumption correct? No answer is possible until the assumption is made more specific. The word *free* in such a general context has no verifiable meaning. It is necessary to specify both the exact influence from which the man is said to be free, and the precise action to be attempted before any judgment is possible.

Let us consider a specific occasion involving choice. A man has been taught that he ought not to steal. He finds himself in a situation where stealing a vaccine would probably save his life. If the vaccine is unguarded and easily accessible, he may be essentially free from physical coercion. But he is certainly not free from other types of coercion. His environment, his previous experience, and his heredity are all contributing coercive forces. Heredity provides an almost unsurmountable instinctive drive toward personal survival; his previous experience of being taught not to steal provides an opposite drive, and his current environment provides the basic dilemma. His subsequent action will be the result of a complicated automatic weighing of the alternatives to produce a maximization of the comfort possible from the situation. What he does will depend on his previous personal and genetically stored experience, on the information he has about the situation, and on his predictions of his future feelings of satisfaction or remorse. There are a host of factors tending to make him steal the vaccine and another host of factors tending to keep him from stealing; his act is the result of an automatic weighing of these factors. The process of weighing alternatives he describes by the phrase "making a choice," and it occurs automatically. If it does not, that is if he "refuses" to choose or is unable to, then he is classed as abnormal, neurotic, insane, or incompetent.

A man's behavior either is, or is not, influenced by current and previous conditions. In the first case his behavior is predictable when enough information is available. In the second case his behavior is random. It is impossible to imagine a case which is not either predictable, random, or some mixture of the two. There is no case left which can correspond to free will; it is a term that corresponds to nothing in the world of observation.

The indeterminacy principle was once hailed as an entry for free will into a deterministic world. Clearly it is not such an entry because it affects measurably only particles smaller than molecules. It would be possible to arrange a machine whose operation would be controlled by the behavior of, say an electron. This machine would not behave deterministically in the classical sense, but it would not have free will either. Its behavior would be random within an easily computable pattern.

A man's behavior is, in principle, predictable. In practice a man's behavior can be predicted with fair accuracy by those who have sufficient information about him and his situation. Man retains one freedom, and this is the only freedom he needs—the freedom to learn from experience. Moral behavior, that is, behavior to maximize the probability of survival of the individual and the species, is not only desirable but necessary for survival. Behavior is automatic; it is frequently immoral because the organism does not have the information necessary to insure moral action. Even when such information is known, the behavior is frequently immoral because of the blind drive of egocentricity inherited from the past.

A man has no "free will" in his actions. They are influenced by the interactions between the man and his environment. Nevertheless, a man is responsible for his actions. If a man's behavior threatens the survival of the tribe, the tribe will react automatically to change his behavior. If he survives the first tribal reaction, his behavior on a second occasion will be automatically controlled by his total experience, which now includes the recent tribal reaction. On the second occasion his automatic comfort-maximizing process may produce a change from his previous behavior. The process seems unjust, but nature is concerned with survival, not justice.

What has been written here so far about the ethics of man is not dependent upon his status as most intelligent and most ferocious animal. The same procedure would lead to an ethic for wolves or horses. Clearly the ethics of man would change slightly according to conditions, and the ethics of an extraterrestrial being might be very different from the ethics of man.

Man is unique on earth because of his highly developed nervous system. This is a device of fairly recent evolutionary development, say about a million years, and its operation is still rather uncertain. In brief, man is subject to a class of malfunctions called loosely "neuroses" or "nervous breakdowns," and temporary or permanent insanity. Such occurrences are not unknown among the other animals, but they are less prevalent. Part of man's problem of survival is to retain his personality when subject to great stress, say the terror of battle. To a lesser extent, men undergo in ordinary life traumatic experiences, say the death of a loved one, which put great stress on his delicate and unstable nervous system. The retention of personality, that is, personal salvation, has been a concern of man throughout recorded history. Since man, like all things living, is subject to an inexorable drive for survival, the word "salvation" has acquired an eternal aspect. But it is the temporal, earthly aspect of salvation which concerns us here.

The great religions of the world have concerned themselves with this ultimate need of man. They have developed liturgies and ceremonies to support man's unstable personality through the great crises of life: birth, puberty, marriage, and death. At times of mental stress a man must not think, for a recurring cycle of thought without beginning or end may close on itself and cut the brain off from external stimuli. Under anxiety a man needs things to do with his hands and body, rituals which are automatic to him. He needs to be surrounded by his friends and neighbors, to be reminded of the trials and triumphs of his ancestors. He needs the words of consolation and advice from the great teachers of the past. He needs the psychotherapy of a liturgy.

The great religions have tried to do all this. They should be judged by the gentleness and sincerity of their effort to better man's condition on earth. It is hard for the thinking man to forgive their pretense of knowledge on eschatological things, of that day of which it has been said, ". . . No man knoweth, no, not the Son, but the Father." But the thinking man must not reject religion because its mystical aspect repels him. Thinking men make up only a tiny fraction of mankind, and the emotional needs of the others far outweigh the intellectual needs of the thinkers.

The thinking man must not reject traditional religion because other men need it. Furthermore, the thinking man must not reject traditional religion because he also needs it. The same liturgy which is white magic to the ignorant and a precious sacrament to the mystic can be emotional food and a pragmatic survival technique for the thinker. From the other side, a man should not be barred from the church, because, by accident of heredity and experience, he is color-blind to mysticism. In the same way that constant attention to the natural law is needed for physical survival, so also is constant attention to the moral law needed for personality survival. The man who concerns himself with the natural law only one day a week will not survive long physically. Those who concern themselves with the moral law only one day a week lower the probability of personality survival. A system something like the monastic offices is needed to remind the ego seven times a day of the demands of the moral law. The periods between the reminders will provide laboratory exercise in the practice of the moral law.

The great religions provide a survival technique for man. Behind a filmy veil of mystical poetry lie the massive bulwarks of man's greatest fortress against his greatest enemy—the brute of his own nature. Those who think the veil is the fortress have lost nothing, for the fortress is still there. But those who abandon the fortress to lose the veil have abandoned all.

Argument

Science and ethics both give advice on behavior. The source of this advice is human experience, the purpose of the advice is human survival as individual and species, and the advice is as accurate as human prediction, no more and no less. Many ethical teachers infer ethics from the concept of God; this essay infers the concept of God from human experience with behavior and its consequences. Derivation of ethical rules from intuition or from a priori principles is not convincing.

Propositional functions of the form, "X is good," have no verifiable meaning until they are modified to the form, "I predict that X will be found good for the purpose of attaining end Y under condition Z." The end Y and conditions Z must be inferred and supplied before the statements of many ethical teachers acquire verifiable meaning.

Science can advise man how to attain an end. There is one end observed to be common to all normal men—survival as individual and species. This essay postulates the following definition: ethical behavior for man is that pattern of individual and collective conduct which maximizes the probability of survival as individual and species. An act is classified as ethical or unethical according to its consequences. The classification will vary depending on the information available. Classification of future acts requires prediction of the consequences, and therefore can be no more "certain" than the prediction itself. This definition of ethical behavior is operationally equivalent to the traditional view that ethical behavior is conduct according to the will of God.

Postulates: There exists an external world as source of sensations. The external world behaves regularly in a pattern describable by natural laws. These laws are unknown, but models of them may be constructed. Successful prediction is the criterion of a valid model.

1. There exists a pattern of behavior toward nature that maximizes man's probability of survival as individual and species. Such behavior is termed *rational*.

1. Part of man's natural environment consists of other people and other living things. There exists a pattern of behavior toward other living things that maximizes man's probability of survival as individual and species. Such behavior is termed *ethical* or *moral*. It is a special case of rational behavior.

2. This rational behavior pattern is unknown, but may be inferred from models of natural laws. The laws of Newton constitute a model of the corresponding natural laws.

2. This ethical behavior pattern is unknown, but may be inferred from models of natural laws. The laws of Moses constitute a model of the corresponding natural laws.

3. From Newton's laws a man can infer that if he jumps off a high building his probability of survival will be decreased. The laws predict future events and any advice must be inferred.

3. The laws of Moses give advice directly. "Do no murder" is an abbreviation for "The act of murder decreases the probability of survival of man as individual and species."

4. Successful models of natural law are often popularly known as "laws of nature." Invention (or discovery) of a "law of nature" often occurs suddenly after long study. A photism may occur.

4. Successful models of natural law which relate to behavior toward other living things are often popularly known as "ethical laws." Invention (or discovery) of an "ethical law" often occurs suddenly after long study. A photism may occur.

5. Early models of natural law were often anthropomorphic. The models have developed from the naïve forms of the early Greeks to the sophisticated forms of today, and will continue to develop in the future.

5. Early "ethical laws" were often anthropomorphic. The models have developed from the naïve forms of the early Hebrews to the sophisticated forms of today, and will continue to develop in the future.

6. The ancient Greeks had men who were particularly skilful in developing early models of the natural law. These experts were called *philosophers*. These philosophers were careful to state that their words were not merely their own but were dictated by natural law.

6. The ancient Hebrews had men who were particularly skilful in developing "ethical laws." These experts were called *prophets*. These prophets were careful to state that their words were not merely their own but were dictated by the personification of ethical law.

7. The "natural" language of models of the natural law is mathematics.

7. The "natural" language of the "ethical law" is myth and parable.

8. The criterion of successful models of the natural law is correct prediction as compared to subsequent experience.

8. The criterion of successful models of the natural law which relate to behavior toward other living things is correct prediction as compared to subsequent experience.

Gentleness and loving kindness are considered positive contributions toward survival and are included in ethical behavior. The quantity to be maximized is the sum of the weighted probabilities; the weighting factors are to be estimated from observation. The simple verbot often found in ethical rules is an abbreviation for, "This act decreases the probability of survival of man as individual and species." This essay attributes the source of ethical rules to observations of society as crystallized in legend and aphorism. Ethics is thus a special activity of the sociologist. The procedures of science and ethics not only run parallel, but are basically the same procedure.

Chapter XV

The Status of Science Today

Basic and applied research. Motivation of scientist. Directed and undirected research. Contract research. Classified research. Education of future scientists. Inadequacy of present schools. Recommended changes in secondary schools. Expansion of schools. Training of science teachers. Motivation of students toward science. Representative current problems of science. Over-population. Law of Malthus. Control of personality. Loyality of the scientist. Survival of man as ecological problem.

Consideration of the present status of science requires that the subject be divided into two parts: *basic science* and *applied science*. Basic science (often called "pure" science) concerns itself with the postulation and testing of partial models of the natural law of the universe. Applied science concerns itself with the use of models to make predictions which are of direct use to the general population. Engineering is the applied branch of physical science. These "definitions" are abstractions from the history of scientific thought and are not mutually exclusive. A particular research project always has both aspects present even though the researcher is chiefly concerned with only one aspect. Einstein was directly concerned with basic science when he postulated and tested the model leading to the expression $E = mc^2$, yet this same relation is useful in the production of nuclear bombs and power from nuclear sources. The Manhattan Project was directly concerned with the development of a weapon, but also contributed greatly to basic science. Both basic and applied science are aspects of a single technique which contributes to the survival and comfort of man. The contribution of basic science is often subtle and long range—the contribution of applied science is usually more obvious and immediate.

The relationship between basic and applied science is symbiotic. Neither can be neglected without impairing the other. The cosmotrons of today which are necessary for basic research on the nucleus are possible only because of the industrial development of materials and electronic components. On the other hand, the development of nuclear weapons was possible only because of the high level of basic physics. Government and industrial makers of policy regarding research must understand that applied research will produce results only when guided by well-validated models provided by basic research.

Attempts have been made to classify scientists as pure scientists or applied scientists on the basis of their supposed motivation. According to these stereotypes, the pure scientist is motivated by a driving curiosity with no regard for his personal welfare or the public good; the applied scientist is motivated by a desire to serve mankind. This dichotomy is too extreme to be useful in classification. Scientists, whether basic or applied, have the same motivation as other dedicated individuals. Scientists work at science for the same reason that poets write poetry and physicians treat patients—because it gives them personal satisfaction. Scientists are no better at analyzing the sources of their satisfaction than anyone else. Some will cite the satisfaction of curiosity, others the satisfaction of public service.

From observation of the biological world one infers that satisfaction is a feeling which accompanies and follows the process of eating, reproduction, and other acts which are necessary to continued survival. It is the medium of exchange whereby actions necessary to ultimate survival are rewarded immediately. Presumably only those wolves who were immediately rewarded for eating by a feeling of satisfaction took the trouble to eat enough to keep alive. The activity of the scientist must also be rewarded immediately by this feeling of satisfaction, for few men can maintain a difficult activity supported only by the abstract knowledge that the activity will provide an ultimate personal or public good.

This feeling of personal satisfaction is the only effective motivation for creative men in any field, whether it is poetry, science, or industrial production. Economic rewards have little effect on creative individuals, and history is full of examples of struggling poets, ragged students, and sleepless inventors who follow their desires regardless of their economic state. The industrial chemist who stuffs his briefcase with experiment reports so he can work in the evening and the physician who goes on night calls are both motivated by personal satisfaction, not by economic desires. Military mercenaries have never been noted for their bravery, and scientific mercenaries are not noted for their creativity.

Scientists have their price, but, above the subsistence level, the price usually is not money paid to them directly. The most exacting part of their price is their insistence on choosing their own research subject. Some scientists are satisfied by specifying their field, such as physical chemistry, electronics, or statistics; others insist on specifying the type of problem. Obviously, the scientist's success in this sort of bargaining depends on his ability and reputation. The able young scientist is faced with the choice of doing precisely what he wants to do at no salary at all, or doing precisely what someone else wants him to do at a fairly large salary. Specific government or industrial projects allow the least choice; academic institutions allow the most choice, and for this reason academic institutions get most of the best men although their salary scale is usually much lower than the industrial scale.

Industry also has difficulty in getting and keeping creative scientists because industrial research projects often give little satisfaction to the scientist. The industrial scientist is fairly contented while developing a new product or making a definite improvement in an old product. But some industrial projects are concerned only with producing a change in the product so that the advertising department will have some new triviality to shout about. The scientific personnel of such projects soon start asking themselves if their hard work could not be better used elsewhere—say in cancer research.

A scientist can be bought with good apparatus and research equipment. In most fields the apparatus needed for research today is so expensive that an individual cannot possibly provide his own. Hence he must go where the apparatus is, and there is intense competition for positions which provide access to unique apparatus. A man interested in controlled high-energy nuclear research must work directly or indirectly for a government because the highest-energy accelerators available today are all government financed. Theorists are sometimes attracted by good experimental apparatus because they wish to be close to the source of new data and in a position to suggest new experiments.

When the scientist has a choice of several locations where he can do research in his chosen field, he will start considering the living conditions for his family and himself. His salary will influence this factor somewhat, but his choice is more concerned with good schools for his children and congenial friends for his wife than with economic factors. If he and his friends have salaries adequate for modest comfort, he seldom concerns himself with economic matters. The way to a scientist's heart is not through his pocketbook.

Until about 1940 almost all basic research was done by single individuals or by groups of men dominated by a single personality. These men conducted research in whatever interested them, limited only by the cost of equipment and assistants. Such costs were usually small enough to be borne by a private institution or even by the researcher himself. Except for a few researchers with independent incomes, foundations, and some public-supported research stations, most basic research prior to 1940 was carried on in university laboratories. The typical researcher was a university professor, and his main income was his professorial salary. Universities supported research by providing laboratories, supplies, and technicians, and by sponsoring a system which required each would-be professor to produce acceptable research as evidence of his suitability for a professorship. Industrial and governmental laboratories before 1940 concerned themselves almost entirely with applied research aimed at the development of a specific product or the removal of an existing difficulty.

Since 1940 and the penultimate war there has been a profound change in research, especially in physics. Much of the most basic physical research now requires apparatus that costs millions of dollars and needs hundreds of men for operation and maintenance. Only a few affluent universities, large corporations, and national governments can afford this equipment. The United States Government has built national laboratories at Brookhaven, Oak Ridge, Argonne, and Los Alamos to provide such apparatus, and research men at neighboring universities can work at these laboratories and share some of the running time of the apparatus.

The existence of research projects with large budgets and hundreds or thousands of workers has raised the question of the productivity of directed research. With most kinds of human activity—business, government, or military—the purpose of the activity is known, and it is axiomatic that a well-planned program will aid in its attainment. But the essence of research at the forefront of knowledge is that no one knows what will happen next, and plans must be revised continually. For an analogy, one can imagine an explorer traveling in an unmapped country.

In the past, important basic discoveries were made during the course of the most unlikely activities of researchers indulging their curiosity. Scientific knowledge as of 1940 was a totality reached by thousands of investigators, each motivated by his own purposes whether practical or impractical. This great number of unbridled and undirected curiosities gave a random character to the totality of research which tended to prevent either a neglect of an area or an inefficient concentration of too many investigators in another area. Most of the scientific knowledge of today was obtained by this *laissez faire* procedure, and scientists are naturally concerned that a change in procedure may retard the rate of discovery. Scientists, of course, favor a planned and extensive effort to find the cause and cure of cancer. But they are very much aware that the key to the cause of cancer may be found, for example, by an obscure botanist trying to find out why so many four-leaf clovers occurred in one corner of his backyard. Nature is so interrelated that the clue to the behavior of a star in the next galaxy may be found by a geneticist studying the propagation of fruit flies.

During the last twenty years the practice of "research under contract" has spread until it has permeated almost all regions of endeavor. If, for example, the Department of Defense feels the need for data on the effect of gamma radiation on polystyrene, that department may contract with the Department of Physics of Blank University to measure these effects. Blank University receives a sum of money and agrees that two members of its staff and four graduate students will work on the problem for two years. The graduate students are paid by the contract and frequently can use parts of the work for their thesis research. The staff members are paid by the contract for the portion of their time spent on the work. The Department of Defense receives quarterly reports on the results of the work, and the researchers involved also present the results for publication in the regular scientific journals.

Contract research has many advantages. The universities benefit by receiving money to support their research laboratories. The university staff members benefit because they are provided with paid technical assistants to help with their research. The graduate students benefit by being paid so they can support themselves and their families during the several years of their graduate work. The Department of Defense benefits by getting the data it needs. The public benefits by this contribution to its corporate safety. Despite this marvel of symbiosis, worried voices arise questioning the ultimate effects of this system. The basic concern is that too many researchers will be involved in directed research and thus reduce the random character of the total research effort.

It is known that undirected research produces an observed rate of discovery; it is not known whether directed research will increase or decrease that rate of discovery—a decrease is feared. The success of directed research since 1940 (nuclear weapons, etc.) is attributed to the accumulation of results from undirected research during the previous century. There is fairly general agreement that caution is necessary, although one might expect serendipity to operate as well during directed research as during undirected research. The governmental agencies which award contracts have attempted to mitigate any possible effect of the increase in directed research by accepting some contracts for basic research which are directed only in a very general sense. Recent studies by methods of operational analysis suggest that directed research is sterile unless preceeded or accompanied by undirected basic research. It is suggested that about 20 per cent of *any* research budget must go for undirected basic research in order that directed research may be successful over long periods of time.

During time of war a nation tries to keep its plans and resources secret from the enemy. Nowadays scientific discoveries and inventions are fundamental to a nation's defense. Reports of scientific discoveries and inventions are therefore "classified," that is, they are kept secret from everyone except those who are directly concerned. This sounds very sensible, but in practice it rapidly gets out of hand. No one knows what item of scientific fact may be useful to the enemy, so practically all scientific reports are classified. Once they are so marked, it is almost impossible to get them declassified again. Even when direct legislation and military commands order such declassification, individuals and boards hesitate to take action lest they inadvertently release valuable information.

There is universal agreement among scientists that classification seriously retards the rate of scientific discovery. It also seems obvious that *some* classification is necessary. Scientists usually feel that it is better to classify too little than too much; security officers usually feel just the opposite, and so far the security officers have had their way.

The teaching of physical science and mathematics in the schools of the United States is grossly inadequate for the needs of current research in physical science, a fact not known to the average citizen. The man in the street judges science by the success of its applications, and the United States has been quite successful in applied science. In nuclear power, nuclear weapons, nuclear experimentation, and jet aircraft the United States is well advanced. In rockets and space research the United States is rapidly overcoming its neglect of this field before 1938. But in theoretical physical science the situation is just the reverse. Let us look closer at the record of the United States in producing nuclear weapons. It is true that United States industry solved the production problems, but the theory which guided that production came mostly from men who were educated in Germany, Italy, England, Hungary, Denmark—everywhere except in the schools of the United States. With the exception of the work of Willard Gibbs and a few contemporary researchers, the contribution of the schools of the United States to physical theory has been negligible. The United States builds the world's biggest accelerators, but the theories which accompany the experimentation are largely developed by men who did not attend the public secondary schools of the United States.

The failure of our schools may be evidenced by the small number of Nobel Prizes in physical science awarded to men educated in the United States. The number of Nobel Prize winners in physical science, per 100 million of population, is: England, 58; Germany, 50; United States, 25. These numbers are obtained by taking the total number of such winners from 1901 through 1959 and dividing by the population of the country in 1930. The contribution of the United States in recent years has improved, but this reflects the troubled condition of Germany and England rather than an improvement in our education system.

Another item of evidence that all is not well with education in the United States shows itself in the matter of Rhodes scholars. Oxford University expects a Rhodes scholar to take the B.A. degree in one of the honors schools. Native Englishmen who study for the honor degree usually come directly from English preparatory schools. The Rhodes scholar from the United States usually has a degree from a United States college. Even so, he has all he can do to keep up with his younger English classmates. The schools in his own country, both secondary and collegiate, have prepared him so poorly that he must work hard to compete with an Oxford freshman. In competition with other Rhodes scholars, the student from the United States finds himself seriously handicapped. Sixteen per cent of the Rhodes scholars from the United States attained first honors as compared with 33 per cent of the Australian Rhodes scholars and 34 per cent of those from New Zealand. As a source of honor students, the United States college is definitely outclassed by the Australian and New Zealand schools.

The most important single reason for the inferiority of our graduates in science is that mathematical preparation for serious study is not given early enough. No quantitative science can be taught in an efficient way until the student has mastered calculus. Currently, most students in the United States complete elementary calculus in their fourteenth year of school. The technical student in a European secondary school completes the same preparation in the twelfth year. This two-year delay is a fatal handicap and by itself is sufficiently serious to account for the poor showing of the United States among the Nobel Prize winners in the physical sciences. In physics and chemistry, a man's peak creativity occurs before the age of thirty. The typical European student receives his university degree when he is twenty-four; the typical student in the United States receives his PhD. at twenty-seven. This leaves the researcher of the United States with a productive period only half as long as that of his foreign competitor.

The teaching of mathematics in primary and secondary schools must be reorganized so that each student who plans to study physical science or engineering in college can attain a working knowledge of calculus by the the end of high school. Table X-2 shows a possible sequence. It would be advisable to require these mathematics courses of *all* students who plan to enter college. The cause of the split in modern culture deplored by C. P. Snow is that most scientists can read the language of mathematics and most humanists cannot. As Latin was the scholarly international language of the Renaissance, so mathematics is the scholarly international language of sophisticated thought today. This fact has led to a peculiar unidirectional diffusion of modern knowledge. The physical scientists and others who read both mathematics and verbal language readily can understand the writings of the historians and (sometimes) the poets. But the reverse process seldom occurs; few historians and poets can read modern science, which requires mathematics for its expression. Mathematics courses through calculus are

Table XV-1

Curriculum for Science Students

Subject	High school credits	University credits
English Composition	15*	0
English Literature	15	0
Foreign Language	24	12
Foreign Literature	12†	0
History	12	6
Fine Arts	12	0
Mathematics	24	42
Science	30	48
Philosophy	0	6
Theology	0	6
Major Field	0	24
Total credits	144	144

* One credit equals approximately 36 hours of class and study. In order to earn the scheduled 18 credits each 16-week semester a student must spend about 40 hours each week in class and study.

† To be read in its original language.

the "children's diseases" of learning, and one who has not been exposed to them cannot consider himself completely adult. Those who have never studied the basic concepts of mathematical analysis have no appreciation of the extremes of technique required for precise thinking. Our forefathers were confident that a knowledge of the three R's was necessary for everyday life. In the world of today the third R for the competent citizen must include at least calculus. Half the problem of our split culture is that our future scientists are taught too little history and poetry. The other half is that our future historians and poets are taught too little science and mathematics; they are trying to understand a culture without troubling themselves to learn its dominant scholarly language.

Table XV-1 shows a recommended curriculum for science students during secondary school and undergraduate university training. Table XV-2 shows the science part of the curriculum in detail (the mathematics part of the curriculum has already been shown in Table X-2). The same curriculum is recommended for all students in the college of arts and sciences of a university. Such a requirement would repair our split culture in short order.

It will be noted that there is considerable emphasis upon the study of foreign language. A reading and speaking knowledge of foreign language is a useful skill, but this is not the reason for the emphasis here.

In terms of education, the main value of the study of a foreign language lies in its unique contribution to an understanding of the principles of the

Table XV-2

Curriculum for Science Students

Subject	High school credits	University credits
Astronomy	3*	0
Geology	3	3
Economic Science	3	3
Political Science	3	3
General Physics	6	0
General Chemistry	6	0
General Biology	6	0
Analytical Chemistry		3
Organic Chemistry		3
Physical Chemistry		3
Atomic and Nuclear Physics		6
Psychology		6
Sociology		6
Zoology		6
Microbiology		3
Botany		3
Total credits	30	48

* One credit equals approximately 36 hours of class and study

communication of thought. A basic aim of all serious education is a comprehension of the distinction between a concept and the words or symbols used to describe that concept. The person with only one language is at a hopeless disadvantage in such a task. The color yellow can never be appreciated by itself, but only as one of a series, by comparison with red and blue. Many of the critics of language study have themselves studied foreign languages and appear to be unaware that this study has contributed much toward their ability to think. Having color vision themselves, they recommend colorblindness for others.

The increase in population requires maximum use of buildings, laboratories, and equipment. One suggestion is that schools operate throughout the year with only brief vacations. Such a procedure may provide maximum efficiency in the use of buildings but care must be taken that it does not also provide minimum efficiency in the use of teachers and students. Accelerated programs are especially inefficient in the long run. The student who has attended college classes almost continuously for three years may be compared to the man who raced through the Louvre in seven hours and nineteen minutes; he said the floors were too slippery to permit greater efficiency. It is possible to learn one subject very efficiently in a few weeks—but if this subject is followed immediately by a different subject in the next few weeks, one is providing optimum conditions for erasure of knowledge of the first subject.

In primary school most learning is done in class; in secondary school some learning is done outside of class; in college two-thirds of the learning is outside of class, and in the graduate school almost all learning is done outside of class. The English univerisites are well aware of these facts—they have three rather short terms per year and the three rather long "vacations" are used for study.

To attain a reasonably optimum system, the entire year would be divided into six terms of about eight weeks each. Each student and each teacher would attend alternate terms; a second group of teachers and students would use the equipment during the "off terms." The student would use the recess periods for study, reading and writing assignments, and for field work. The teachers would use the recess period for study, research, and writing. No student and no teacher should ever be permitted to attend two successive terms. No competent young student should ever be permitted to work for money during his student career—a small amount of working for experience might be permitted. A society which wishes to survive in a competitive world must not permit its competent young people to waste their time and energy—the most valuable national resource—in work which could be done by less competent young people or older people beyond the creative years. It is as important for a nation to provide education without cost to competent students at all levels as it is to provide public roads, public water, and public safety.

There is great concern at present over the large expansion of schools and colleges required during the coming years. Certainly planning is needed, but the consternation of some viewers is unwarranted. At present, less than 1 per cent of the gross national product goes to education; the country can afford to increase this manyfold. The increase can be charged to the "defense budget"—its presence will hardly be noted, and, in any case, it belongs there because education is the most powerful of all weapons. Financing education is a federal matter, a matter too important to be left to individuals or communities. Talented children occur in poor families and poor communities. These young people are the most valuable of all national resources, and each one must receive the best educational opportunity our civilization can provide. A nation that leaves the quality of education available to a youth to be decided by the economic status of his family or community hardly deserves to survive.

More teachers will be needed in the years ahead, but much could be gained by a more efficient use of the existing teachers by delegating many of their routine activities to administrators, stenographers, and technicians. On the other hand, our students have been permitted to delegate too many of *their* responsibilities to the teachers. A small portion of today's students essentially teach themselves, but most students have to be shown, led, and even coaxed. These students are not to be despised, for they are typical members of the human species. Mankind is a poor thing, but he is all we've got and we have to make do with him. Teachers at all levels must be adept at wheedling out more effort and more accomplishment than most students will volunteer, and this is not done with a television set. The supply of competent students is completely inadequate for the needs of our society; therefore no effort can be spared in trying to train the less competent.

The Physical Science Study Committee, organized in 1956, is a group made up of college and high-school teachers of physics and industrial and academic research physicists, and has concerned itself with a modernization of the secondary-school course in physics. More recently, similar committees have been formed by chemists, mathematicians, and biologists to consider changes in the content and approach of secondary-school courses in those fields. It is to be hoped that this trend will continue, and that the professionals of other fields will unite with their college and high-school teachers to maintain adequate and modern instruction at both college and high-school levels.

The graduate schools of our colleges also have their part to play in providing better secondary-school teaching of all subjects. They must provide the courses which secondary-school teachers need to extend and modernize their knowledge. Frequently these courses must be given at an undergraduate level since most secondary-school teachers are not highly specialized. It is the lack of such "content" courses taught by specialists that has led to the proliferation of the worthless "methods" courses prevalent in many colleges of education.

The motivation of more students to choose a career in science has been suggested as a means of increasing the supply of scientists. The use of high-pressure Madison Avenue methods may motivate young people into science, but it will not provide the intelligence and drive needed to stay there. The percentage of the population capable of first-class accomplishment of any sort is fixed and considerably smaller than the demand. An aggressive campaign may increase the number of science students, but the only competent ones will have been diverted from the supply of physicians and other intellectual professions. The only effective way to increase scientific manpower is to increase the efficiency of the fixed supply by making sure that creative scientists do not waste their time on administrative or other work which can be done by others.

The current status of basic physical science may be illustrated by listing some representative problems. Nuclear theory lacks an accurately quantitative model applicable to all nuclei. About thirty fundamental particles have been observed experimentally; it is possible to arrange these in systematic tables, but no single model exists which correlates their properties. In macrophysics there exists as yet no satisfactory four-dimensional unified field theory.

The problems of applied physics, like the problems of applied biology and sociology, all stem from one source—overpopulation. The law of Malthus (which says that population increases faster than the food supply) has not been invalidated; the day of reckoning has merely been postponed. Whether it comes in three generations or ten generations, its eventual arrival is equally certain if the population continues to increase.

After the flood, as recorded in the book of Genesis, man was told, "Be fruitful and multiply and replenish the earth." It is nowhere recorded that man was told to overpopulate the earth. The "rights of the unborn" certainly include the right to be born into a world where starvation is not the norm. It is possible to postpone the Malthusian day of reckoning for a few more generations by learning to eat corn stalks mixed with cellulase and to drink diluted sea water. But why? There is no earthly reason for such behavior, and, despite the statements of certain false prophets to the contrary, no heavenly reason either. The fruits of such behavior are obvious. A prophet that advocates behavior leading to starving children is easily classified.

Owing to our unbridled desires and wasteful habits, we are already near the limit of our supply of fresh water, fertile soil, large trees, coal, oil, and many metals. Within limits it is possible to desalinate sea water, refertilize soil, grow more trees, use nuclear and solar energy, and find substitutes for depleted metals. But again, why? The historic reason for wanting big families—soldiers to defend the clan—is valid only within a definite limit. Overpopulated countries such as China and India cannot possibly defend themselves in a modern war. A country that has to spend all its energy to keep its citizens from starving has no will or weapons to defend itself.

The outstanding problem of political science today is the steady decrease of personal freedom of each citizen of the world. Contrary to popular opinion, this decrease is not the result of the evil will of dictators or the spread of pernicious doctrines. These things are symptoms, not causes. It is a simple law of nature that personal freedom decreases when population increases. If unchecked, the increasing population will necessitate restrictions on personal freedom far beyond the nightmares of the most sadistic tyrant.

By the year 2000, if the population continues to grow as at present, we can predict restrictions of the following sort: No privately owned automobiles will exist because of the cost of metal, oil, and fuel. Tobacco will be available only by prescription; the land will be needed to grow food. Meat will be available only at astronomical prices because meat requires an inefficient use of land. Travel will be permitted only by special arrangement for a publicly approved purpose; energy per capita will be limited and not available for travel for pleasure. Meals will probably be communal because family cooking involves waste. Water will be rationed. Apartment space per family will be limited to about two small rooms because ground area will be needed for farming, and wood and building supplies will be inadequate. Each citizen will have to work at the job he can do best regardless of personal preference. Industries will be so interlocked by supply problems that the individual executive will have little freedom of decision. Competition will be illegal because it is wasteful of men and materials. Strikes will be illegal and suppressed by military force. Such restrictions are the inevitable results of overpopulation. It will make little difference what type of government exists; the laws of scarcity economics apply to all forms of government.

Politicians, theologians, and advertising agents have long known that man is only partly rational; most of his decisions are emotional or instinctive. Having recognized this fact, the unholy three have sought to play upon man's emotions for their own ends. Their motives—in some cases—may have been good, but the results are deplorable. If mankind is to survive much longer, each man must be aware of the irrational drives of emotion and instinct within himself. The church has succeeded in convincing some men that their natural tendency is toward sin—perhaps the schools can convince some men that their natural tendency is toward emotional irrationality. The saint fears his own tendency to sin; each man must learn to fear his own irrational tendencies. The notion that emotions may be used for good ends is dangerous; so long as any man trusts his emotions those emotions are available for use by any unscrupulous person.

National and international governments must somehow be so built that no action can be taken when emotions are aroused. Political leaders, theological leaders, and advertisers could cooperate by appealing to man's reason rather than to his emotions. With current nuclear armament, one national tantrum could depopulate the world.

The outstanding problem of applied psychology is the control of personality. The outstanding problem of sociology is who will control the controllers. The danger inherent in such knowledge makes nuclear and biological warfare seem trivial. But ignorance of such matters is more dangerous than knowledge. Control of personality is no new thing; individuals have made fumbling attempts to control their own personalities for ages. The tranquilizers of today had their milder precursors in the tobacco of yesterday and the wine of the ancients. The effects of more concentrated chemicals such as hashish and opium have long been known; the effect of lack or excess of thyroxin and other hormones is a more recent discovery. Extreme deficiency of the B vitamins affects the personality. The study of the influence of mescaline, lysergic acid, and similar compounds is just beginning.

In addition to the direct chemical attack on personality there is the environmental approach, which ranges from ordinary education and ordinary advertising through unscrupulous indoctrination and vicious propaganda to that total effort called "brainwashing." The only protection against such indoctrination is a previous indoctrination. The earliest indoctrination usually prevails because the ideas recorded in the brain become progressively less erasable as time goes on until elderly people find it quite impossible to "unlearn" concepts.

Individuals have never had any choice of the indoctrination they received from the tribe. Indoctrination, to be successful, must not openly contradict observable facts. "You can't fool all the people all the time." Nature stands aloof from man's internecine warfare. The cool neutrality of nature is a haven for the individual from the lies of organized society and the alleged friendship of the gods. Education in science indoctrinates the individual with the authority of nature—the scientist accepts no other ultimate authority. Even when the organized might of society concentrates on brainwashing the individual, the last conscious spark of personality can whisper silently, "*Eppur si muove!*"

The scientist has given his first and greatest loyalty to the law of nature; after that comes his loyalty to mankind, and after that a tangled skein of loyalties to nation, family, sect, and lesser things. Most men and most scientists are fortunate, and do not find themselves in situations requiring important choices between conflicting loyalties. When an occasional scientist must publicly choose his loyalty, his choice often outrages the patriots whose emotions rise to nothing higher than nationalism.

When a new species is introduced to a limited region as, for example, when a closed lake is stocked with trout, the general trend of events is easily predictable from well-validated models of ecology. The population increases until it reaches equilibrium with its food supply and its natural enemies, unless the whole population is killed off first by its own poisonous excreta. A half-million or so years ago such a species—man—appeared within a limited region—the surface of the earth. The great mass of mankind will always be bound near the surface of the earth by the inexorable chains of gravitation. The fantastically large amount of energy needed to rocket even one man off the earth guarantees this. For every man who leaves the earth, one million others will have to stay behind to support the industry needed to build and fuel such rocket ships. The surface of the earth is a closed environment, and the bulk of those born on the earth will remain there.

Therefore, we can expect that the human population of the earth will increase until man's food supply can increase no more or until man is killed off by his natural enemies or his own poisonous excreta. All three of these ends are within sight. The limit of the world's food supply will be reached within a few generations. Man's natural enemy increases daily in number and lethality—for man's natural enemy is himself. And man's poisonous excreta, the radioactive dust of his weapons, rains silently and invisibly from the stratosphere, upon the just and the unjust. The survival technique of the tyrannosaurus was ferocity; it is extinct. The survival technique of the dodo was passive resistance; it is extinct. The survival technique of man is science. . . .

Index